WHERE INDIA GOES

Diane Coffey and Dean Spears are visiting researchers at the Economics and Planning Unit of the Indian Statistical Institute in Delhi, assistant professors at the University of Texas at Austin and executive directors of r.i.c.e., a research institute for compassionate economics, online at www.riceinstitute.org.

WHERE INDIA GOES

*Abandoned Toilets, Stunted Development and
the Costs of Caste*

Diane Coffey and Dean Spears

HarperCollins *Publishers* India

First published in India by
HarperCollins *Publishers* in 2017
A-75, Sector 57, Noida, Uttar Pradesh 201301, India
www.harpercollins.co.in

2 4 6 8 10 9 7 5 3

P-ISBN: 978-93-5264-565-7
E-ISBN: 978-93-5264-566-4

Typeset in 11/15 Berling LT Std at
Manipal Digital Systems, Manipal

Printed and bound at
MicroPrints India, New Delhi

For Palak,
and for all the children who will be born in India
before the end of open defecation,
whenever that may be

Contents

List of Figures

Foreword by Angus Deaton

It is hard to think of anything more important than how we treat our children. In recent years, we have come to understand that what happens to children ricochets through their lives, and that many of society's ills could be addressed if we were to take more care of the youngest among us. Nowhere is this more true than in India. As recently as five years ago, Prime Minister Manmohan Singh reiterated his earlier statements that 'the problem of malnutrition is a matter of national shame'. More than a third of the children in India in 2015-16 were abnormally skinny and abnormally short. Not surprisingly, Indian adults are among the shortest in the world, and although things are improving for both children and adults, change is glacially slow. According to one calculation, at the current rate of progress, it will take 250 years for Indian women to catch up with British women, even if the latter get no taller than they are today. All of this is in spite of the fact that per capita incomes in India have been growing much faster than in the past, making the Indian economy one of the world's star performers.

This is an intellectual puzzle for economics and for global health, but for Indians themselves, it is an ongoing catastrophe. Millions of children alive now, and millions still to be born, will live lives that are less good and less productive than they should be; and in too many cases, some will die. It is one of the great achievements of this book that it works on so many levels, untangling the intellectual puzzles with the verve of a good mystery, telling us the stories of the people who are suffering, how they live their lives, why they think and behave as they do and what sort of interventions might help or hurt them. It brings national and local data to bear, so that we know how to generalize from the stories. It is at once intellectually rigorous and deeply humane. It is worthy of the trust and cooperation of the authors' many friends and collaborators in India, as well as the women and children who let them into their lives.

The book focuses on an understudied aspect of Indian life, the widespread custom of open defecation. It has long been known that open defecation is a bad thing, yet more attention has often gone to other matters, like vaccination and the provision of safe water. In public health, the great historical achievement was to break the faecal–oral link, the contamination of drinking water by human waste. John Snow's work on cholera in London is the most famous of many examples in Europe and the United States. Providing safe water in difficult conditions is a good deal easier and cheaper than the construction of safe sanitation systems, and great progress has been made on water in India and around the world.

But, as this book shows, open defecation is still a serious problem, especially where population densities are high, and people are walking in, and children playing in, their neighbours' faeces. This is a classic externality problem – which economists and development professionals understand well enough – but it turns out that the obvious solution – the provision of latrines – doesn't work in India. Beliefs about purity, cleanliness, caste and untouchability generate a steel fence that prevents change in traditional ways of disposing of human faeces.

I shall refrain from further spoilers. The book is a joy to read and not the least of its pleasures is spending time with the sharply and affectionately drawn people that we meet along the way.

The book also carries important lessons about how to study development, and how to turn commitment and educated intelligence into the sort of research that has a real chance of changing lives for the better. It is always hard to work in a country that is not your own. There are ethical problems in telling people what to do, especially when resources are unequal, as is often the case between agencies and those whom they wish to help. Those problems are especially troubling when the researchers know little about their subjects, assume that their training or experience elsewhere equips them to give advice, or believe that all development problems are amenable to modern technocratic fixes.

Coffey and Spears took a very different tack. They set up an institute in India with help from collaborators and friends and immersed themselves in the lives of the men and women who live in an impoverished part of Uttar Pradesh. It is clear that without their communication and understanding, and without being able to talk to the people they were working with, this book could not have been written. Of course, the policy conclusions that are so beloved of the development industry would perhaps have been much sharper than the honest puzzlement ('a problem that we do not know how to solve') and recommendations for further research that this book delivers. But such conclusions would likely have been wrong. Real understanding is the only hope for science to speed a better future.

Princeton, March 2017

1 | Introduction

Unlike most babies born in villages in Sitapur, Ramila's daughter had a name from the time she was born. Naina. Like most babies in Sitapur, a district in Uttar Pradesh, Naina was born small: only about 2.5 kilograms. She became sick with diarrhoea when she was about one month old.

Ramila took Naina to many doctors. They gave her medicine each time, which Ramila put into her daughter's mouth with a dropper. One evening, Naina was so sick that Ramila rushed her to town even though she had no one to accompany her. The doctor told her that nothing more could be done for the baby. 'Diarrhoea had won.' Alone and exhausted, Ramila returned home at eleven thirty at night. She had walked nearly 6 kilometres to her village from Subedarganj, a small settlement on the outskirts of town where the cycle rickshaw driver had dropped her off.

A couple of days later, Naina was still alive, but she was still very sick. Someone from her village suggested to Ramila that she take the baby to the 'rickshaw-wale' doctor – like many of the others, not actually a trained health professional – in Samaypur, a town about 35 kilometres away from the village. Ramila's sister-in-law lives in Samaypur, so knowing they would

1

have a place to stay, she decided to give it a try. When she got down from the bus in Samaypur, Ramila asked around until she found the rickshaw-wale doctor.

The doctor told Ramila to stop giving the baby any sort of milk: no cow milk, no buffalo milk, no breast milk. He sold her some oral rehydration powder and another medicine, which Ramila thought made the baby sleepy.

Next, Ramila went to her sister-in-law's house, where they welcomed her by buying a Pepsi. One of her relatives wanted to give Naina some Pepsi. Ramila protested, saying, 'Please don't, it will bother her stomach.' But her relative did not listen; he put a couple of drops of Pepsi on Naina's tongue and she seemed to like it.

Later, as Ramila was nodding off to sleep, Naina started to cry a little. It made Ramila sad to hear Naina crying; she did not want her baby to be hungry. So, against the doctor's orders, she nursed Naina for a short while. They both fell asleep. In the morning, when Ramila woke up, Naina opened her eyes briefly, then closed them again. Ramila patted Naina for a few moments until she was sure she was asleep.

Then Ramila and her niece went to defecate in the open.

When they came back, Ramila's sister-in-law was holding the baby in her lap. As Ramila washed her hands, her sister-in-law asked whether Ramila had given the baby any milk. At first Ramila lied and said no, but seeing the concern on her sister-in-law's face, Ramila admitted that she had. Her sister-in-law's eyes began to tear up.

Ramila understood that something terrible had happened while she was gone. In anger and frustration, she threw down the steel lota that she had been using to wash her hands.

Ramila had to call a neighbour from her village to pick her up in Samaypur because you are not allowed to bring a dead body on the bus.

<center>~~~</center>

A few months after Naina died, a mason and some labourers came to Ramila's village and told people that they were building latrines. The money for the latrines originated in Delhi, where politicians, bureaucrats and development professionals planned to eliminate the problem of rural open defecation by paying for latrines for those households that did not already have them. The Government of Uttar Pradesh, where eight in ten rural households defecate in the open, packaged the Central government's latrine money with other types of infrastructure, such as paved roads, drains and electricity poles. State politicians and bureaucrats awarded the entire package to villages, including Ramila's, on the basis of applications submitted by their village leaders.

The brick structure that was built in front of Ramila's house was not the latrine that the planners in Delhi had in mind. Ramila's 'latrine' consisted of three brick walls, a solid cement floor and a nearby round cement slab that was meant to be the lid for an underground pit. This latrine had no seat, no pan, no door, no roof, no pipe and no pit. Corrupt bureaucrats and politicians had pocketed the money that would have been used to provide all the parts of a real latrine.

But, Ramila did not mind at all that she and her family had not received a remotely functional latrine. She gathered some tarpaulin sheets and sticks and used them to fashion a roof and a door. Then she piled the kande, or dung cakes that she uses for cooking, inside the new little building. There, her fuel stayed dry and neatly stacked until she needed it. She found the round pit cover to be a convenient surface. By washing dishes on the new cement slab, rather than on the ground in front of the house, she and the dishes got less muddy.

Ramila's neighbours did not mind their incomplete latrines either. Some, like Ramila, used the little structures for storage. Others used them to wash clothes. Still others used them as private places for women to bathe. Many just ignored them. Only one out of the at least 100 households in Ramila's village took it upon themselves to complete the construction of their latrine and then use it for someone to defecate in.

Everyone else continued doing what they had done their entire lives, and what their parents and grandparents had done before them: every morning, and sometimes in the evening, they walked to the fields, the roadside, the orchard or the banks of the pond and defecated in the open. They walked away from their own houses, though in densely populated rural Sitapur, nobody is ever very far from somebody else's house. They left their faeces on the ground, spreading the same sort of germs that may have caused Naina's diarrhoea.

Brief lives in India and around the world

Ramila was not alone in her struggle to keep her child alive, nor in her grief when that effort failed. According to the World Bank's World Development Indicators for 2012, the year that Naina lived and died, forty-three out of every 1,000 babies born in India died before their first birthdays. We told her story not because it is unique – sadly, Naina was not the only baby who died that spring from a group of twenty infants living nearby whom Diane was following – but because Ramila described it so vividly.

An infant mortality rate measures the fraction of babies who die within their first year of life. India's is high. Out of the 194 countries with World Bank data from 2012, 150 or around 77 per cent had an infant mortality rate lower than India's. India's infant mortality rate was three times those of China, Brazil and Russia. It was higher than Bangladesh's, Kenya's and Rwanda's. India's infant mortality rate was on a par with Uganda's and Myanmar's.

Part of the reason why infant mortality in India is high is that many Indians are poor. Babies are indeed far more likely to die in poorer countries than in richer countries, on average. But poverty is not the only cause of infant death. In fact, infant mortality in India is about 20 per cent higher than the international trend predicts for a country with India's GDP per capita. If India merely had as many infant deaths as other countries with its GDP per capita, over 170,000 fewer babies would die each year – an *excess* of infant deaths approximately as large as the *total* number of infant deaths in South and North America combined. Because about one-fifth of all births now occur in India – and many more than one in five infant deaths do – India's especially high infant mortality is a central fact of the human condition in our times.

For Sitapur district, where Naina was born, the Indian government's 2010–11 Annual Health Survey reports an infant mortality rate of 82 deaths per 1,000 live births. If, in 2011, the World Bank had counted Sitapur as its own country, its infant mortality rate would have ranked 190th out of 195 countries, slightly worse than Mali and the Democratic Republic of the Congo. The only countries with a higher infant mortality rate than Sitapur would have been Chad, Somalia, the Central African Republic, Sierra Leone and Angola.

Perhaps Sitapur _should_ have counted as its own country. Its 2011 population of 4.5 million people was the same as the Central African Republic's in that year. Sitapur had three-fourths as many people as Sierra Leone and half as many as Somalia. Over 40 per cent of countries in the World Bank data were home to fewer people than Sitapur, which is only one of the many districts in Uttar Pradesh, which is only one of the many states in India.

───

Life in India has been improving quickly in recent decades, even in Sitapur. The 1964 _Sitapur Gazette_ records a recent past in which residents were afflicted by malaria, cholera, smallpox and even bubonic plague. Thankfully, some of these diseases have been eradicated or are now rare. India's most recently estimated infant mortality rate is less than a quarter of what it was in 1960, when the World Bank data begins. The average person in India is richer, lives longer, eats better and is able to send her children to more years of school than ever before. Similar rapid improvements have been happening throughout the developing world, thanks to many reinforcing causes: scientific knowledge such as the germ theory of disease, public health investments, economic growth and the spread of literacy.

That so many changes would result in better, healthier lives in India is no surprise. The surprise is that India is not doing even better than it is. The Indian economy has recently experienced many years of rapid economic growth. Household surveys show that more and more Indians own assets such as fans, cellphones and motorcycles.

So why is economic progress so incompletely reflected in India's poor infant health? Why do so many more babies die in India than in developing countries with similar economic profiles? This puzzle is well-known to researchers, and is not limited to infant mortality. We are far from the first to notice that India's record of human development – that is, of health, education and freedom to choose a good life – lags far behind the quality of life offered by many poorer countries. In 1996, Vulimiri Ramalingaswami, Urban Jonsson and Jon Rohde called attention to the fact that children in India are shorter, on average, than children in sub-Saharan Africa, who are poorer, on average. In 2013, Jean Drèze and Amartya Sen noted that although India is richer than its South Asian neighbours Bangladesh and Nepal, it suffers worse outcomes in infant and child mortality, teaches a smaller fraction of its women to read and has a higher fraction of underweight children.

A person's reaction to these facts turns out to be a test of her political persuasion. Indian nationalists simply deny them, sometimes inventing pseudo-scientific positions that expert consensus on the evidence is wrong and that the health of Indian children is actually just fine. Political theorists have long recognized that nationalism always requires a little bit of fiction and forgetfulness of historical facts. In the era of big data, perhaps this maxim requires elaboration: Nationalism now also requires failing to collect, tabulate or understand statistics.

The political right characteristically responds to this story by saying that what is needed is more economic growth. By continuing to pursue economic growth, the country's markets will eventually improve India's abysmal health and education indicators. The political left sees India's human development indicators as justification for a strong welfare state. If Indians are suffering worse outcomes than are evidently economically feasible, the state should step in to deliver public goods and private benefits.

We think there is something to the hopes of both sides: The Indian state does far less for its poor citizens and its rural citizens than it usefully might. A much stronger social safety net is compatible with economic growth that improves lives. A stronger social safety net is also an appropriate response to growing inequality, which threatens social cohesion and probably undermines democratic pressure for public services that matter for everyone.

What we do not see in either prescription is an *explanation* for the paradox. Economic poverty does not explain India's poor human development: The very puzzle is that India offers worse lives than poorer countries. Nor can the failures of the Indian state explain poor human development. India's poor governance, political structures and relatively small role of the state in many rural lives are not ideal, but nor are they radically worse than in poorer countries.

The distance between the human development that India achieves and the human development that its economic wealth predicts represents much suffering, many deaths and a disproportionately large fraction of the stunted children and inadequate sanitation found in the world today. So, this gap is a big deal for anyone, anywhere in the world, who cares about human well-being. It requires an explanation.

In this book, we consider one important piece of the puzzle: sanitation in rural India. The fact that Ramila and hundreds of millions of other people defecate in the open every day is a human development disaster. It is indeed a market failure, and it is not being resolved by the Indian state. Both of these facts are important. But neither explains why sanitation in rural India is so much worse than in other developing countries. Rather, poor sanitation persists in rural India because of unique social forces – in particular, caste.

Many people look forward to a modern, prosperous India. But it may not be possible to accelerate India's future without engaging with the illiberal forces of caste and untouchability that are still part of India's present. Open defecation in rural India is a globally special case that helps us understand how social inequality constrains human development.

An increasingly Indian problem

Open defecation is the sanitized, scholarly term for what about a billion people worldwide do with their faeces. They walk to a field, a roadside, a riverbank, an orchard, a forest or another place outdoors, squat down and relieve themselves on to the ground. Then they walk away, leaving the germs to infect somebody else. Naina died while Ramila was defecating in the open, but if Naina's diarrhoea was caused by faecal germs, as we suspect, they probably came from someone in another family.

The United Nations Children's Fund (UNICEF) and the World Health Organization (WHO) collaborate to produce global statistics on sanitation. Their 2015 Joint Monitoring Report estimates that 13 per cent of the world's population disposes of its faeces in this dangerous way. The other 87 per cent of people use some sort of latrine or toilet, ranging in expense and comfort from a simple hole in the ground that is covered up and re-dug every few weeks, to a flush toilet connected to a sewer system or a septic tank.

Although open defecation is still practised by the poorest people in many developing countries, it is increasingly a uniquely rural Indian problem. The last national measurement of open defecation in India comes from the 2011 census, which found that 53 per cent of Indian households had no toilet or latrine and did not use a public toilet. The figure was much higher for rural households than for urban households: 13 per cent of urban households lack a latrine or toilet, compared to 70 per cent of rural households. These figures imply that the vast majority of open defecation in India – 89 per cent – takes places in villages.

The 2011 census also found that the rate of decline in open defecation in India in the prior decade had been very slow: only about 1 percentage point per year in both rural and urban India. The persistence of open defecation is surprising in light of India's rapid economic progress. The World Bank's International Comparison Programme computes that India's gross national income per capita grew at an average of 8 per cent per year between the 2001 and 2011 census rounds. Income growth in India over the same decade was 46 per cent faster than in sub-Saharan Africa and 53 per cent faster than in the world overall.

However, over this period, the fraction of the population using toilets and latrines in India fell further behind the rest of the developing world. Many people in sub-Saharan Africa and other parts of Asia who are far poorer than the average rural Indian nevertheless use a toilet or latrine. According to the 2012 UNICEF and WHO Joint Monitoring Report, only a quarter of households in sub-Saharan Africa defecate in the open. Even in some very poor African countries such as Uganda and the Democratic Republic of the Congo, open defecation rates are less than 10 per cent. In South Asian countries other than India, only 12 per cent of households defecate in the open. In contrast to India, China has all but eliminated open defecation.

India's share of the world's remaining open defecation grows each year. In 1990, about half of the people in the world who defecated in the open lived in India. By 2012, India accounted for 60 per cent of global open defecation. India's population – 17 per cent of the global population – is certainly large, but it is not that large. Because people in other developing countries are adopting latrines and toilets more quickly than Indians are, it is likely that the global share of open defecation that occurs in India will keep growing.

What we learnt by learning about toilets

India was not always an outlier in rural sanitation. There was a time when open defecation was the only thing that humans did with their faeces. Not so many decades ago, rural open defecation rates would have been high in essentially every country. India stands alone today not because it changed, but because the rest of the world did.

The global decline in open defecation is only one of many rapid improvements in human well-being that have defined the past century. Robert Fogel, a Nobel Prize–winning economist, described the world in 2004 as having made three centuries of progress towards an 'escape from hunger and premature death' which he dates from 1700 to 2100. Economist Angus Deaton, also a Nobel laureate, called these sweeping changes humanity's 'Great Escape'. Lives are longer, fewer people are hungry, children are taller, and more people can read and choose how to live their lives, all around the world. These are big advances, and they reflect big underlying scientific, social and economic changes.

These improvements are unmistakable in demographic data. They often reinforce one another. Better early-life health permits children to learn more and, as adults, to earn more, so that they can then provide a better environment for the next generation. Greater social equality means that more girls attend school, have more power over their own lives and become mothers at later ages, and know more about how to keep their children safe from disease.

In a world that is improving so fast, it can be difficult to be sure what, if anything, could further speed these existing trends. Just because the Great Escape is measurable does not mean that it is under anyone's control. This is a central question of our book: Can development efforts add something extra to a world that is already part-way through a rapid Great Escape? If so, how?

The answer may be in the second part of Deaton's thesis: inequality. When Deaton describes demographic trends as an escape, he wants us to remember that many escapes leave somebody struggling behind. The human development of the twentieth and twenty-first centuries is no exception: Escape causes inequality. When infant mortality falls more quickly in China or even in Bangladesh or Nepal than it does in India, it creates inequality among the world's children.

International development is known for asking big questions. In the 1990s, the Washington Consensus asked how to get prices right for development. In the 2000s, the UN collaborated with celebrities to ask how to make poverty history. The evidence-based policy revolution of the past decade summarizes itself by asking simply: what works? Often, the question has been only that simple, presuming a solution that works for everyone. The reality of a fast but uneven and unequal Great Escape suggests two different questions. First, how can change be accelerated in the places and on the issues that are improving only slowly? Second, how can ongoing rapid improvements be pushed to go a little more quickly?

Comparing open defecation in India with sanitation elsewhere makes plainly visible the need to keep these questions separate. To answer them, one must contrast a problem that is found in a slowly improving place against a record of faster improvement almost worldwide. The result can usefully clarify what is important. For example, sanitation was an undeniably central part of how mortality declined and health improved in the countries that are now rich. Differences in sanitation explain many differences in outcomes across developing countries today. So, it is no surprise that what today ranks as unusually terrible sanitation contributes to pushing India off the global trend of improving health and well-being.

But comparing India with the rest of the developing world also reveals that whatever was responsible for improving sanitation elsewhere either has not been available or has not worked the same way in rural India. Such is the dilemma at the heart of this book. Much of the world has experience with drastically reducing open defecation. It is exactly from that international and historical experience that experts have learnt just how important sanitation is and just how harmful faecal germs can be. But the very fact that rural India lags so far behind in sanitation suggests that the experience of the rest of the world may tell us little about how to accelerate the switch to safe sanitation in rural India. If India's leaders, sanitation experts and development professionals want to help rural India become like everywhere else, they must devise a new strategy based on both understanding the consequences of poor sanitation that India shares with other, often past, populations and understanding why rural India remains unique.

In the view from the government offices and the hotel conference rooms of development, poverty bears the responsibility for depriving poor people of access to what they need. Villages are communities where poor people come together to help one another. Poor people lack options to choose among, but experts know how to empower the poor to make themselves and their neighbours better off. Democratic pressure demands that governments make these changes. Development experts are useful because they can apply lessons to one country (or within India, one state or district) that they learnt by being responsible for improvements elsewhere.

All of this may be true in some cases, but open defecation in rural India turns development platitudes upside down. Open defecation initially appears to be an easy problem to solve. Even the most free-market-oriented economist recognizes that sanitation requires subsidy and public action to prevent one family from dumping its germs on another. So, the obvious solution is for the state to distribute free latrines. We agree that free latrines, targeted to people likely to use them, could be a small part of an effective response – in the unlikely case that such a programme could be managed without consuming all of policy attention available for sanitation. But in rural India, poverty itself is not the problem, and subsidized latrines are not nearly enough to solve it. Far too many free latrines are never wanted or never used. Even when they receive a latrine that would be recognized as perfectly functional in other developing countries, people in rural India defecate in the open.

The fact that many people in rural India who receive a government latrine nevertheless choose to defecate in the open surprises many city dwellers. But it is perfectly reasonable to many people in rural north India who can explain to a curious visitor what is wrong with government latrines and why open defecation is a superior option.

There are illiberal ideas in every culture. Unique to Ramila's culture are the particular illiberal notions of untouchability and ritual purity that people in her village would invoke while rejecting a functional government latrine. These are not ideas that will be convenient or comfortable to address for a government which is dominated by higher-caste urbanites – and which perpetuates manual scavenging even in its own investment decisions and hiring practices. Nor are international development professionals likely to bring these issues to the fore: Culturally sensitive development professionals cannot admit that cultures differ. One reason is that it is unacceptable for outsiders to blame the victim by acknowledging that poor people, like rich people, often harm one another. Another reason is that the fact that cultural differences or other place-specific causes could have important effects challenges the role of international expertise.

Left with no other admissible explanation, sanitation experts repeat the claim that people in rural India lack access to latrines due to poverty. A few do. Yet, the standard invocation of access to latrines denies the plain fact that quality sanitary latrines are purchased or made inexpensively in most developing countries. The mantra of access denies the agency that villagers so clearly have.

International development cannot recognize what is unique about Indian open defecation; meanwhile, domestic democratic pressure has no reason to focus on it. It is rural citizens' own behaviour that harms their neighbours, after all. Villagers are not aware that open defecation kills children and so they have no reason to electorally punish their local councils for failing to make their neighbours use latrines. In villagers' minds, open defecation is a far superior choice to storing faeces in a government-provided latrine pit that would need to be emptied by hand, an activity which invokes a generations-old struggle between people who are still too often thought of as 'Untouchables' and those who still too often exploit, exclude and humiliate them. It is no wonder that Ramila was far happier to receive a storage room and washing slab than she would have been to receive a functional government latrine.

A problem that cannot be solved through construction funds, democratic pressure, international expertise, cooperative community engagement, decades of economic growth or subsidy is a problem that will be difficult to fix with the familiar tool kit of development policy.

A book for two audiences

For some readers, this book is about the human development emergency of open defecation in India: a dwindling opportunity to prevent a million or more child deaths before it is too late. For these readers, we are documenting an important case. It was not logically necessary that the ways in which the caste system has adapted and endured in modern rural India would stand against latrine use; that open defecation would be so very bad for child health; and that this would all happen in a densely populated country where over one-fifth of all infant deaths occur. But these did all occur in the same place, in our time. There are reasons to worry about whether the Indian state and international development efforts will supply an effective response.

For other readers, less focused on India's present-day policy challenges, this book is about the paradoxes of development in the early twenty-first century: What scope is there to make life better in an unequal world where conditions are for the most part improving quickly, but in some places and ways, painfully slowly? What important threats to human development does economic development overlook? Is pretending that India is already a liberal society with free markets and equal opportunities a way to make it one? Are there effective methods to motivate improvements in the problems and places that the Great Escape has not yet reached?

The collision of technocratic policy with culture, politics and human choices is a story that has been told before. But it is important enough to tell again – this time, against the background of a growing scientific consensus about the importance of child development and human capital for economic development, and of the interactions of health and wealth. Each chapter in this book is about open defecation, but it is also about something else.

The next three chapters ask why open defecation persists in rural India. Chapter 2 presents the puzzle: Why does rural India have such high rates of open defecation when international comparisons suggest that most people could afford to buy, make or use the same latrines that are eliminating open defecation in sub-Saharan Africa and the rest of Asia? Remarkably, this is often not the first question that sanitation bureaucrats or development professionals ask. To pose this question requires abandoning the sanitized claim that open defecation in India is all about lack of access to latrines and is no different from what happened in Latin America and South East Asia. It requires recognizing that Indian villagers who reject accessible, affordable sanitation options are the most powerful actors in this book's story.

Chapters 3 and 4 ask how development is constrained when it runs ahead of social equality and liberalism. In public health, an enduring debate asks whether economic inequality makes people sick: Does health in a population become worse, on average, as a result of an increase in income inequality? In the case of open defecation, *social* inequality perpetuates poor health for everyone.

Chapters 3 and 4 present a two-part answer to the questions that we pose in Chapter 2. In Chapter 3, we hear from villagers who explain that the pit latrines provided by the government are dirty and impure. We consider what this means in a society in which the same system of ritual purity and pollution is applied to objects, such as pit latrines, and to people from certain castes. Many villagers think that having a simple pit latrine is inconsistent with maintaining a home that is ritually pure. Open defecation, in contrast, has no such negative connotations.

Chapter 4 considers the question of why the few latrines that rural Indians have built for themselves are so much more expensive than the latrines that the government builds. At the core: Villagers reject affordable latrines because their pits must eventually be emptied by hand. But disposing of human faeces is the work of Dalits. Unfortunately, not enough has changed since Dr B.R. Ambedkar observed decades ago that the power and supposed superiority of the higher castes are tied to avoiding untouchable work. Even today, more than sixty-six years after the Indian Constitution declared people from all castes equal under the law, the vast majority of higher-caste people still find the idea of emptying their own latrine pits unacceptably degrading. And, as in Ambedkar's time, avoiding untouchable labour continues to be a way for Dalits to resist an oppressive social order and, in some cases, to improve their lives. Even where pit-emptying work is profitable, many Dalits would prefer to avoid the humiliation and social exclusion that accompany this work. These add up to compelling reasons for rural Indians to reject the types of latrines that save lives elsewhere.

If the prospect of full latrine pits threatens to continue Dalit oppression because *someone* will have to empty them, and if many people in rural India do not mind defecating in the open, you might ask whether it should really be a policy priority to end open defecation. Chapters 5 and 6 document why reducing open defecation is so important for India's future. They build on a growing consensus among economists that two important dimensions of well-being – wealth and health – cannot be fully understood alone. Chapter 5 reviews evidence for the considerable effects of open defecation on multiple dimensions of children's health. Researchers have found effects of open defecation on mortality, on anaemia and even on the sizes of children's bodies. Reaching this understanding has required the sustained work of epidemiologists, demographers and economists, collaborating across decades and centuries. By focusing on the puzzle of why Indian children are so much shorter than children elsewhere, we emphasize the importance of infectious disease to nutritional outcomes, such as height, which are more commonly associated with food. Humanity's Great Escape from infectious disease remains incomplete.

Chapter 6 explores the economic consequences of India's widespread open defecation. Development in a child's earliest years shapes his economic productivity as an adult. One way that open defecation negatively impacts India's economy is by stunting the cognitive development of future workers. The same diseases that make children short also make it more difficult for them to learn. The result is another generation that grows up to be less productive workers than they could be, who earns less money and pays less in taxes. This research shows that open defecation is not only in the portfolio of the health ministry: The finance minister has good reasons to care about this problem too.

Chapter 7 is about a different type of consequence of open defecation: the loss of dignity experienced by those who would like to use a latrine, but who do not have that option. For a small fraction – but large number – of people in rural India who are very old or disabled, walking to the fields to defecate is difficult, painful or impossible. For those elderly and disabled who are lucky enough to get a latrine, they must live with the burden of having caused their families to make a large expenditure. These are real costs of the fact that, in rural India, open defecation is perfectly normal.

The last two chapters focus on policy responses to open defecation: What do the Indian state and international development do, what they claim to control, and what do we hope they will do? Chapter 8 turns to the sanitation programmes and policies of Indian governments, past and present. Elected governments come and go, but rural sanitation policy remains little more than publicly funded latrine construction. The Swachh Bharat Mission has a bigger budget than earlier sanitation programmes, but it is not importantly different. Unfortunately, there is little democratic pressure to change where a half-a-billion rural Indians defecate.

States develop capacity and power in part through collecting data and developing information systems. Political scientist James Scott warns that states can take this too far, and can exercise too much power over their societies when they rearrange people to fit their own legible schemes. But the rural sanitation programmes of the Indian state do just the opposite: They ignore opportunities to gather useful information on how many Indians defecate in the open and obfuscate this fact with intricate webpages that claim to track construction funds. Although a developmental state reducing its own managerial capacity would appear to be at odds with Scott's worries, the Indian state's approach to sanitation monitoring may be unsurprising when we consider whether there is an effective political constituency against rural open defecation in the first place.

International development agencies also influence sanitation policy. We build on anthropologist David Mosse's observation that even very powerful people in development agencies can do little to control events. So, most of what people in these organizations do is interpret them. The budgets and staff of international development organizations are small relative to the 600 million Indians who defecate in the open. Yet, their public claims about sanitation shape what policymakers, researchers and journalists pay attention to. International development faces a dilemma. First, its most important opportunity to contribute may be with useful knowledge and international expertise; yet, neither professional managers nor academic researchers have the incentives or the resources to answer a place-specific, unsanitary, applied question like how to accelerate the decline in open defecation in rural India. Second, there are no unproblematic sources of political legitimacy for international development: The world has rightly rejected the imposition of undifferentiated global solutions from Washington and New York. However, it is no alternative to automatically endorse the decisions of governments which may or may not be acting in the best interest of all of its citizens. This paradox is deepened when applied to a problem rooted in social inequality: Neither technical experts who advise governments in countries around the world nor India's predominately high-caste, urban leaders may fully understand what emptying a latrine pit would mean to a rural Dalit.

Finally, in Chapter 9 we ask: What strategies might accelerate the decline of open defecation in rural India from its long-standing rate of one percentage point a year? We propose some tentative ideas of our own, discuss some common suggestions we believe will not work and ask ourselves what it means to promote well-being through development policy in a world that is quickly becoming richer and healthier, with important exceptions.

How we learnt about open defecation

We wrote this book because we have been humbled by a problem that we do not know how to solve.* We first started thinking about open defecation in the fall of 2011 while living in Sitapur district of Uttar Pradesh. When we decided to live in Sitapur, we were looking for a place where we could learn first-hand about the poor early-life health and the process of stunting that affect so many children in India. We certainly found it.

The year before we moved to Sitapur, Dean had stumbled upon a library book about sanitation in developing countries. He decided to compile government and demographic data to see whether the Indian government's Clean Village Prize had made an impact on child health. As he was analysing these data, Diane was visiting villages to learn more about the challenges of raising a baby in rural Sitapur. Because average height, at a population-level, is a marker of health in early life, and a predictor of important outcomes in adulthood, we wanted to understand the puzzle of child height in India: Why are Indian children among the shortest in the world?

One thing that was clear from both the health data and from Diane's repeated visits to families with young children is that children in rural north India are very sick. Many of them die young. Those who survive grow up both physically

---

* We have been lucky enough to learn from many people we have met, and from the work of many researchers. Throughout this book, we will often summarize other writers' research and our own. In a set of notes at the end of the book, we provide enough details to look up everything we cite. We also provide a few extra notes and more information on our own research methods.

and cognitively stunted. At about this time, Dean computed that child height and cognitive achievement are much more steeply correlated in India than in the developed world, for reasons we will explore in Chapter 6. On bicycle rides through villages near our house, we encountered pile after pile of faeces, on the roads, in the orchards and in the fields. We asked people if we could peek into their crumbling latrines, built by past government programmes. Latrine after latrine was abandoned, unused.

These experiences led us to assemble all the data we could find on sanitation and early-life health in India and to look more carefully at villagers' sanitation behaviour. As we started to share our findings, we began to interact with development professionals who work on sanitation in government and international agencies, both in India and abroad. Typically, we prepared for these conversations by studying demographic and survey data of the sort that allows us to compare what happens across places in India and between India and the rest of the developing world. We gradually realized that our experiences in north India and the lessons of the Indian data did not match the stories we heard and statistics we saw about other countries. At that point we knew we had a mystery: Why is open defecation in rural India different?

The next step involved good fortune that we still cannot explain. Somehow, a smart, energetic team of fantastic researchers decided to join us in a newly formed research organization, r.i.c.e., to study the causes and consequences of open defecation in India. In August 2013, we began collaborating with Aashish Gupta and Sangita Vyas; in the coming months, Nikhil Srivastav, Payal Hathi and Nidhi Khurana would join the r.i.c.e. team as well. Over the year that followed, this team travelled to many states to understand why India has such uniquely high rates of open defecation. In Sitapur, we trained surveyors from states across north India to ask thousands of people about their defecation habits. The survey team, along with a cook and a scout, visited thirteen districts. Alongside the quantitative data, the seven of us personally interviewed hundreds of villagers and local officials in seven Indian states and in Nepal. Members of the team also visited Bangladesh, South East Asia and sub-Saharan Africa to see, in person, the differences that were so stark in demographic data.

We learnt much from talking with officials and professionals in governments, aid agencies and development organizations. We have also benefited from conversations with academic colleagues at both Indian and US universities and with people working for social equality in India. Many sanitation and health researchers took time to teach us and sometimes to even collaborate with us. The research in this book reflects the effort of many teams – and all of it ultimately reflects the thinking and learning that we are grateful to have been able to do with our collaborators and friends at r.i.c.e.

All the characters in our story – local government implementers, senior government policymakers, academic researchers, high-caste people, low-caste people and international development professionals – respond to their own incentives and often see something different in the problem of rural open defecation from the classic models of the public economics of sanitation. We focus our story on the rural Indians who are both spreading the faecal germs and suffering the consequences. The coming chapters will introduce you to rural men and women who are born into a social system of power and hierarchy that, largely unknown to them, is killing and stunting their own children.

Causes

2 | The puzzle: Why rural India?

It was a raw winter morning. Diane and our research collaborator Nikhil were wearing jackets and sneakers, but Shantanu was wearing only a wet pair of shorts. He was bathing at a hand pump by the side of the lane. When his house was selected for an interview, Diane and Nikhil walked over to see if he would be willing to talk for an hour or so.

They waited for about fifteen minutes, while, shivering in shorts, he squatted in front of a chula, or open stove, and held a pair of jeans towards the flames. Even though they still looked half wet, Shantanu put on his clothes and invited Diane and Nikhil to sit in front of another house across the street, leaving the women to cook at the chula.

Shantanu's family lived in the second house too. He and his wife have seven sons, most of whom live in the village with them, and some of whom have children of their own. So, the family not only occupies the newly constructed two-storey brick-and-mortar house where he was drying off but also rent the house across the street. The two-storey house that Shantanu had recently built was by far the most impressive of the crowded cluster of modest homes at this edge of the village.

Compared to the thatched roofs of most of the other houses and the piles of dung cakes strewn about, the paved village lane with built-in drains that bisected the neighbourhood seemed incongruous. We could tell at a glance that the lane had been paved by a government village development programme. Another telltale sign that the programme had been awarded to this village was the newly painted latrine buildings that lined the side of the road. Each one had the date and the official cost of construction painted on the side.

One of the latrines belonged to Shantanu's family. As far as Nikhil and Diane could tell, without measuring tape, it was well-constructed, according to government specifications. The above-ground latrine building, or 'superstructure', was made of bricks and cement with open spaces at the top for ventilation. A ceramic pan with a water seal was cemented into the floor. A pipe led from the pan to a four-foot-deep pit lined with bricks. Below ground in the pit, gaps intentionally left between the bricks would, in principle, allow water to seep hygienically into the ground. A second pit had also been dug next to the first one.

Judging by the looks of things, we hoped Shantanu would tell us that his family had begun to use their government latrine. Instead, we learnt that the latrine, which had been built about a year before, had never once been used for defecation. When we looked inside, we found some laundry soaking in a bucket of soapy water and a scrubbing brush for cleaning the clothes.

Open defecation kills infants and stunts the physical and cognitive growth of those who survive. Given the urgency of the problem, many people's first reaction upon learning that open defecation in India is widespread and hugely damaging for health is to suggest building latrines for families like Shantanu's. This chapter, and the two that follow, explain why that first reaction is sufficiently incomplete as to be wrong.

The next three chapters turn to the puzzle of why Shantanu and his family defecate in the open in spite of the fact that the government built them a functioning latrine. This chapter poses the puzzle. We will see that many oft-invoked explanations for India's open defecation are false: India's high rates of open defecation cannot be explained by the fact that India is a developing country, nor by its poverty, its access to water, its levels of education, its governance, or the poor quality of latrines that the government often provides. Other countries achieve better sanitation with far worse inputs.

We will start by asking what we can learn about open defecation in India by looking at what happens in other countries. In neighbouring Bangladesh, for instance, the Demographic and Health Surveys (DHSs) find that latrine use in rural parts of the country has become almost universal in the last twenty years, increasing from 67 per cent of households in 1994 to over 95 per cent in 2014. Unfortunately, the comparison between India and Bangladesh is not anomalous: India has a higher fraction of households that defecate in the open than almost any other developing country. Ninety per cent of countries that are poorer than India also have lower rates of open defecation.

Looking within India reveals a surprising fact that sharpens this puzzle: In many cases, people in rural India do not use the latrines that they own. Of course, most people in rural India do not own a latrine, even though it would be inexpensive to buy or make the sort of latrine that people use in other countries.

But a temporary focus on the minority cases of rural latrine owners is instructive because it helps rule out the 'access' fallacy once and for all.

In this chapter, we introduce the SQUAT (Sanitation Qualify, Use, Access and Trends) survey, which asked, rather than households, where they defecate. Because most surveys have not been designed even to acknowledge the possibility that people do not use a latrine they own, we had to collect new survey data to explore this dimension of India's sanitation crisis. The fact that so many people who own latrines reported not using them suggests that national estimates of how many people in rural India defecate in the open are almost certainly too low. It also means that giving everybody a latrine would not be enough to eliminate open defecation in rural India – or even to come particularly close.

Open defecation in Bangladesh, India's poorer neighbour

Bangladesh is a place where open defecation has caused a lot of problems. It was the birthplace of the first cholera pandemic – a disease spread by faecal pathogens that leads to swift death from dehydration. Thankfully, over the past twenty years, successive waves of credible survey data from Bangladesh have shown a steep decline in open defecation. By 2014, less than 5 per cent of rural Bangladeshi households reported defecating in the open.

In the fall of 2013, we visited Bangladesh along with our r.i.c.e. colleagues to learn about the use of latrines among India's poorer neighbours. Driving around Rajshahi, a district in Bangladesh which borders the Indian state of West Bengal, we caught a glimpse of a makeshift latrine at the edge of a grassy field, near the edge of a river. Curious about why someone would put a latrine in what seemed like an unpopulated place, we asked the driver to pull over so we could investigate. We piled out of the car and headed down a slope towards the latrine. We learnt that the latrine, and another one like it that was not visible from the road, had been constructed by people living in tents in a migrant worker camp at the bottom of the embankment.

Diane, Dean and Payal stayed with our Bangla interpreter and started talking to the migrant workers about why and how they had constructed the latrines. Aashish and Sangita wandered off in another direction and were intercepted by a migrant worker who spoke broken Hindi. He confirmed that, instead of defecating by the stream that was next to the camp, the workers had indeed dug the pits and erected some tin and plastic bags to make themselves the latrine. One of the latrines had a hard plastic latrine pan; the other used black plastic bags in place of a pan.

The migrant worker had walked across the border to India many times before. Learning that Aashish and Sangita were coming from India, and seeing their interest in the makeshift latrines, the labourer volunteered his observation that people in India rarely use latrines, preferring instead to defecate on the roads and in the fields.

This man already knew what the Indian government appears to ignore: Using a simple latrine does not have to be expensive. Like this labourer, many of the poor people in Africa and other parts of Asia who use latrines are not using expensive pour-flush latrines, made out of brick and concrete like the ones the Indian government promotes. Many of them contain their faeces in holes dug in the ground, perhaps covered by a rock or concrete slab, or by planks of wood to stand on. In fact, the most common type of sanitation facility in Bangladesh in 2014 was pit latrines, which were used by 75 per cent of households.

The poverty fallacy

It is a common assumption that rural Indians defecate in the open because they are too poor to use latrines. However, of the fifty-five countries in the world with less GDP per capita than India – Bangladesh included – forty-six have a fraction of the population that defecates in the open smaller than it is in India.

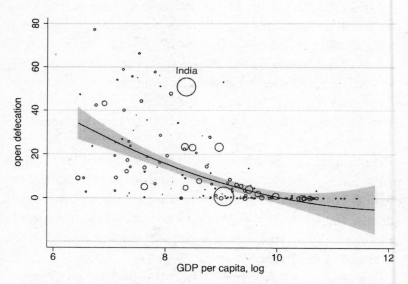

Figure 1. India has more open defecation than other countries with similar GDP per capita

You can see this for yourself in Figure 1. We will see a series of graphs like this in this chapter. Each circle is a country; the vertical axis is the fraction of people who defecate in the open in that country; and the horizontal axis is a candid explanation for India's high rate of open defecation that turns out to be no explanation at all. The size of the circles is proportional to the population of the countries. This scaling reminds us that even though there are a few tiny countries where a higher fraction of people defecates in the open than in India, most of them are comparable in size to Indian districts.

But GDP per capita can be a bad measure of poor families' economic resources in an extremely unequal country like India. If we instead focus only on people who are extremely poor, that is, on people who live on less than the World Bank poverty line of 1.25 dollars per day, we find that twenty-one countries have a higher fraction of the population that is poor than India does. And, as Figure 2 shows, in nineteen of those twenty-one more impoverished countries – over 90 per cent of them – a smaller fraction of the population defecates in the open than in India.

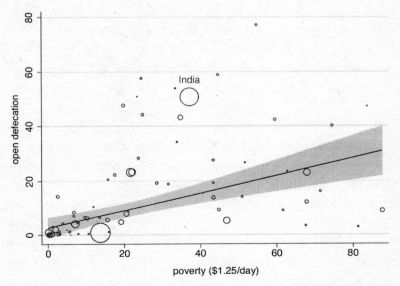

Figure 2. India has more open defecation than other countries with similar poverty rates

Focusing on the poorest people in India and Bangladesh generates an even starker comparison. In 2006, 52 per cent of Bangladeshi households had dirt floors and no electricity. One year earlier, in wealthier India, only 21 per cent of households had dirt floors and no electricity. Yet, among such very poor households in Bangladesh, only 28 per cent defecated in the open; 84 per cent of these poor households in India defecated in the open. If poorer people in Bangladesh and other developing countries can afford to use latrines, people in India could afford it too.

These economic facts have a straightforward explanation: Simple latrines are simply not expensive. A fact this book will visit and revisit is that even though people in India are richer, on average, than people in sub-Saharan Africa, Indians are much more likely to defecate in the open. This means that people in India would be at least as able as people in sub-Saharan Africa to afford a latrine. Within India, Muslims tend to be poorer than Hindus, and rural residents of the north-eastern states are poorer than rural people in the rest of India. But in both comparisons, the poorer groups are considerably less likely to defecate in the open.

The water fallacy

If poverty cannot explain rural India's high rates of open defecation, can lack of water? Over and over, we have heard government officials and the media suggest that rural Indians would use latrines if they had more water to flush and clean them. Indeed, the Swachh Bharat Mission sets itself apart from the earlier government's Nirmal Bharat Abhiyan in part by 'requiring' that water storage tanks be built alongside government latrines.

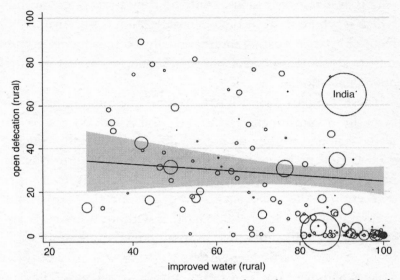

Figure 3. Rural India has more open defecation than other countries with similar access to improved water

But just as in the case of poverty, water scarcity cannot explain India's high rates of open defecation. This is unfortunate. If water were the culprit, the problem would perhaps be much easier to solve. The truth is that it takes very little water to use an inexpensive latrine. The vast majority of rural Indians have a water source very close to their homes. Indeed, the WHO–UNICEF Joint Monitoring Project on water and sanitation finds that 90 per cent of people in rural India have access to what they call 'an improved water source' which in rural India includes piped water, public taps and hand pumps, tube wells and, to a lesser extent, dug wells. In contrast, in sub-Saharan Africa, less than half of people have access to these improved sources of water (49 per cent), but far fewer people in rural sub-Saharan Africa (35 per cent) defecate in the open. In fact, because data is available that focuses only on rural parts of countries – which is where most of the open defecation is – we can see in Figure 3 that comparing internationally, there is no discernible statistical relationship at all between rural water access and rural open defecation.

These comparisons with Africa should be interpreted a little carefully because many latrines in rural Africa do not have a water seal, and so they do not need to be flushed. But digging such latrines is a feasible option in India too. From a health perspective, these latrines are an improvement over open defecation if the holes are covered. Despite this, households in rural India very rarely build latrines without water seals, and so the latrines that are found in rural India require more water for flushing. Nevertheless, gathering a few extra litres of water a day is no longer the hardship that it was in the past: The days of women walking for miles to fetch water in rural India are, thankfully, largely over.

One more piece of evidence that lack of water is not to blame for open defecation in India is the fact that many, many households that have piped water nevertheless defecate in the open. In the 2011 Indian census, almost half of rural Indian households *with* water on their premises do not own a latrine! This is a remarkable fact, which rules out the possibility that these households cannot use a latrine because water is less conveniently available to them than it is to rural people in other countries.

Although there are many good reasons to make sure that everyone has plenty of conveniently located, clean water, the data suggests that water scarcity is utterly unable to explain why people in rural India do not use latrines. Water is simply less scarce in India than in other countries with better sanitation.

The education fallacy

Do people in rural India defecate in the open because they are uneducated or illiterate? Turning again to the international data, Figure 4 shows that twenty-eight countries have adult literacy rates that are lower than India's. As with poverty and wealth, twenty-three of these have lower open defecation rates than India's. Because 82 per cent of countries with worse literacy than India have better open defecation outcomes, it is hard to conclude that education itself is the problem.

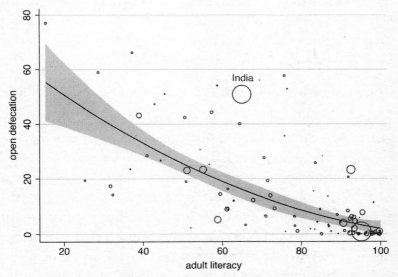

Figure 4. India has more open defecation than other countries with similar adult literacy rates

Similar conclusions emerge from comparisons within South Asia. Among rural households in the 2012 India Human Development Survey, in which someone has a bachelor's degree or more, 32 per cent defecate in the open: just under one-third. Fifty-one per cent of households in rural India where the highest educated adult completed secondary school defecate in the open.

This contrasts with rural Bangladesh in its 2011 Demographic and Health Survey, where 4 per cent of rural households with an adult who completed secondary school and about 1 per cent of those with education beyond secondary school defecate in the open. Only 6 per cent of rural Bangladeshi households are sufficiently uneducated to have no members who have ever completed primary school. Of these least educated Bangladeshi households, a mere 14 per cent defecate in the open – less than half the prevalence of open defecation among households in rural India in which someone completed a bachelor's degree. Lack of education is not the explanation.

Governance has not been the solution – nor is it to blame

Another misplaced explanation that we sometimes hear is governance: India's open defecation is so exceptionally bad, people say, because the Indian state does a poor job of delivering sanitation programmes. Unlike some of the other suggestions, we understand where this one is coming from. Indeed, we will devote all of Chapter 8 to the role of the Indian state. As we will see, the Indian state has consistently misdirected its energies and neglected to take a strong stand against the social inequality that remains important in Indian sanitation. Moreover, what the state does – funnels money into latrine construction – is undoubtedly diminished by corruption.

But the question we are trying to answer is why open defecation in India is so much worse than in other developing countries. Governance in India is bad, but is it worse than in Afghanistan, the Democratic Republic of the Congo, Haiti, Liberia, Myanmar, Pakistan and Sierra Leone? Each of these countries has a smaller fraction of the population that defecates in the open, and each also scores as less democratic or more authoritarian than India in the polity database constructed by political scientists Monty G. Marshall and Ted Robert Gurr.

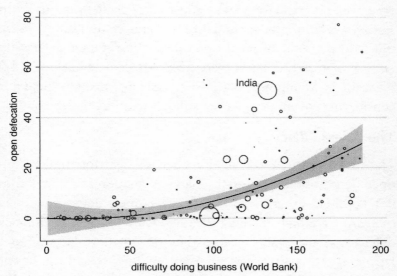

Figure 5. India has more open defecation than other countries with similarly rated governance

The World Bank measures governance using its widely cited Ease of Doing Business Index. As Figure 5 depicts, forty-seven countries are rated as more difficult to do business in than India. Thirty-nine of these – 83 per cent – have a lower rate of open defecation.

The failure of the poor governance explanation is also clear in comparisons across Indian states, as Dean and economist Amit Thorat have documented. States which are generally described in the news as relatively capably governed, such as Gujarat and Tamil Nadu, have rural open defecation rates (more precisely, household latrine non-ownership rates) in the 2011 census of 67 per cent and 76.8 per cent, respectively. These are not far behind the 78.2 and 82.4 per cent of Uttar Pradesh and Bihar, states in the northern plains that are nobody's idea of governance superstars. In contrast, the north-eastern states – which are poor and marked by governance challenges, but are in some ways culturally dissimilar to the large central states – have much lower rates of rural open defecation. Open defecation rates as per 2011 census were 15.9 per cent in Sikkim, 14.0 per cent in Manipur and 15.4 per cent in Mizoram. So, after considering governance, we are still left without an explanation.

The access fallacy

The most common explanation that we hear for rural India's open defecation is not much of an explanation at all, and does not consider other countries or why open defecation is so *comparatively* high in India. People assume that rural Indians defecate in the open because they do not have 'access' to a latrine; if they had 'access' to a latrine, they would use it. For example, a UN website writes: '2.5 billion people – roughly 37 per cent of the world's population – still lack what many of us take for granted: access to adequate sanitation.'

We have trouble understanding what this means. 'Having access to a latrine' typically appears to be used as an unthinking synonym for 'owning a latrine'. But these are not the same. Despite Diane's suggestions, Dean does not own the sort of wide-brimmed hat that could prevent another round of heat stroke during fieldwork; but he clearly has access to one, if he chooses to buy it. Almost any household in India could choose to buy or make the sort of pit latrine that most of the poorest people in Bangladesh and Africa use, or they could choose to use something better.

It is true that using a rudimentary latrine is not as pleasant as using an indoor toilet. It is also true that the latrines provided by the Indian government are, in principle, nicer and more expensive than many of those constructed by households in other developing countries, but, in practice, they are sometimes incompletely or shoddily built. This is in part because of corruption and in part because people do not demand better: If rural households like Ramila's wanted a working latrine, they would be less likely to tolerate local politicians giving them anything else.

Nevertheless, friends who have heard the story up to this point sometimes try to salvage the 'access' explanation: Perhaps the latrines that people in rural India receive from the government are unusably awful; their quality is just too low. What this explanation misses is that if people in rural India really wanted to use pit latrines of the sort the government gives away, they could spend some of their own money or labour to complete or spruce up the shoddily built latrines that the government provides.

One minority group of rural Indians unambiguously has access to a latrine: people who live in a household that owns one. What do those people do?

Until this point in the book we have been using public, typically government-sponsored, data sources like the census and the Demographic and Health Surveys to estimate how many households and persons in rural India defecate in the open. But these data are fundamentally about households, not about the people in them. In other words, the Indian censuses count how many *households* own latrines, not how many *people* use them.

The Demographic and Health Survey (DHS) provides a better, though imperfect, approximation because it asks about what sort of defecation facility a household *uses*. Compared with the census, the DHS presents a more accurate picture of the level of open defecation in a village if there are households, like Shantanu's, which own a latrine but do not use it at all. However, the DHS asks one general question about household behaviour; it does not ask about the behaviour of individual family members.

The consequence of the way that India's national surveys have asked about open defecation is that we do not actually know how many rural Indians defecate in the open. Although this question is central to understanding progress towards reducing disease transmission in rural India, it turns out to be surprisingly difficult to answer with government data. Beginning in 2013, our team at r.i.c.e. started to put together a survey that would help understand this missing piece of sanitation data in India. Along with almost thirty surveyors and support staff, we all carried out the SQUAT survey to study Sanitation Quality, Use, Access and Trends in rural north India.

The SQUAT survey team travelled to villages in thirteen districts of five states: Bihar, Haryana, Madhya Pradesh, Rajasthan and Uttar Pradesh. The places that we chose are important for understanding open defecation. Open defecation is very common in these states; collectively, they are home to at least 30 per cent of all people worldwide who defecate in the open. The 2011 census shows that 80 per cent of rural households in India that do not own a latrine reside in one of these five states.

By late spring 2014, the SQUAT surveyors had learnt where 22,787 people defecate and had collected data about latrine ownership and other characteristics for 3,235 households. Our team had hauled backpacks, survey forms, pots, plates and sleeping bags by train, bus, jeep and tempo. One by one, the details from our pink, yellow and white survey forms were entered into the computer, then entered again to double-check. By early summer, we were ready to finally learn what nearly 120,000 pages of survey forms would reveal.

The answer was clear: Open defecation is common, even in families that own a latrine. In 18 per cent of all of the households we surveyed, at least one person defecated in the open and at least one person used a toilet or latrine. In other words, in this 18 per cent of households, some people were using the latrine and some were not. This suggests that many households are misleadingly classified by the census, the DHS and any other data source that classifies entire households into either latrine users or open defecators without a toilet. These surveys have overlooked this important third category of households. They are a minority, but they teach us something: If you ask about open defecation for each member of the household, you find more of it.

The SQUAT survey data found that over 40 per cent of households in the sample that had a working latrine had at least one member who nevertheless defecates in the open. This statistic is a useful one because the people from these households who defecate in the open unambiguously had the option not to. Of course, any household that can afford and has space for a 3,000-rupee latrine such as in South East Asia or sub-Saharan Africa also has the option not to defecate in the open. Still, the conclusion is particularly unavoidable for households in the SQUAT data with a working latrine: Open defecation in India is not merely a problem of lack of access to latrines.

What would happen if the government built a latrine for every household?

We have established a puzzle about latrine use in rural India. When we learnt these facts, we were surprised, and also curious: What makes latrine use in rural India so different from the rest of the developing world? Satisfying that curiosity is the goal of the next two chapters. But first, we should notice that this paradox has already taught us something important for a rural sanitation policy oriented towards latrine construction.

The Indian government has been subsidizing latrines in villages for more than three decades. The Central Rural Sanitation Programme (CRSP) began in 1986 and provided subsidies for latrine construction for 'below poverty line' families. There were other components to the programme's written guidelines, such as the construction of community toilets, education awareness raising activities and the 'conversion of dry latrines' into pour-flush latrines (we will revisit this topic in Chapter 4), but the focus was on constructing pit latrines.

The Total Sanitation Campaign (TSC), launched in 1999, was intended as a 'demand-driven' scheme in which households request money from the government to build latrines themselves. Still, like its predecessor, this programme also focused on latrine construction and spent little money or effort on promoting latrine use. Moreover, as we will explain further in Chapter 4, rural Indians think that the cost of a usable latrine is many times more than what the government offers. So, even if applying for and receiving the money were not fraught with implementation constraints, many people simply would not have been interested.

One innovative aspect of the TSC was a cash prize to the local governments of villages that eliminated open defecation.

The data suggests that this did some good in the early years of the programme, but the incentive quickly fell apart as state and Central government judges began awarding prizes to villages that had not remotely eliminated open defecation. States with particularly poor governance, like Uttar Pradesh and Bihar, gave up on the 'demand-driven' design of the programme altogether and spent the TSC money hiring contractors to build latrines for families like Shantanu's, many of whom never wanted them to begin with.

Andrés Hueso, a sanitation researcher, has closely studied the statistics and reports of the TSC. Comparing the 2001 and 2011 rounds of the Census of India, he notes that the fraction of rural households that own a latrine went up by about 9 percentage points – but population growth was great enough that the total number of households without a latrine *increased* by more than eight million.

These numbers contrast sharply with the 46-percentage-point increase in sanitation coverage reported over this period by the Central Ministry of Drinking Water and Sanitation. That means that even if every single latrine that was added between 2001 and 2011 were a *government* latrine (so there were zero privately constructed latrines), it would still be the case that millions of latrines reported built by the government are 'missing'. As Hueso summarizes in a paper with Brian Bell, 'These numbers imply that only one in five latrines reportedly constructed since 2001 was in place in 2011.'

We have no way of knowing how many of these 'missing latrines' were constructed and not used, partially constructed and then deconstructed by the recipients, or never constructed at all. Despite the failures of the Total Sanitation Campaign, the Nirmal Bharat Abhiyan, launched in 2012, was a brief, nearly identical programme. The biggest difference was that the government announced that it would spend more money to build each latrine than it had under the TSC.

This history offers important evidence about what would happen if the government again tried to distribute free latrines. We know that many of them would never be built and many more would never be used. But even previous latrine construction programmes have been small compared to the prime minister's 2014 plan to build latrines at an average rate of one per second to eliminate open defecation by 2019.

———

Another way of learning about what would happen if the government were to build a latrine for every household that lacks one involves making statistical projections using data on latrine use among the owners of existing government latrines. If we want to know whether, say, a forty-year-old man belonging to a low-ranking caste with six years of education in a medium-sized village in eastern UP would use a government latrine if he had it, we can match him to other forty-year-old men of similar caste rank and education in medium-sized villages in eastern UP who *do* own government latrines, and assume that he would be about as likely to defecate in the open as they are. Of course, this demographic matching procedure cannot precisely predict what would happen: People who agree to own a latrine, rather than, say, dismantle it for parts, are probably more likely to want to use one than people who do not. Such caveats would cause this procedure to underestimate the open defecation that would still exist after the government distributes latrines.

Applying this method to the SQUAT data, we projected that if the government built a working latrine for every household in rural Bihar, MP, Rajasthan and UP, about two-thirds of the new latrine recipients would not use them. Rural open defecation in these states would still be above 50 per cent.

So, latrine construction will not be enough to end open defecation. At best it is incomplete as a solution to poor sanitation; at worst it, as we will see in this book, reinforces unhelpful beliefs about what a latrine must be. Unfortunately, in practice the Indian government's sanitation policies have implicitly assumed that people do not use latrines merely because they cannot afford to build them. Yet, we will see in the following chapters, and as Shantanu's story suggests, the cost of latrine construction is not the binding constraint.

Solving a puzzle requires setting aside the pieces that do not fit. In this chapter, we have examined and discarded several pieces. Open defecation is far more common in rural India than in other developing countries. More open defecation cannot be explained by more poverty, less water or less education. Three decades and four reincarnations of government latrine construction programmes, dedicated to improving 'access' to latrines, have failed to importantly reduce open defecation.

The SQUAT survey also documented that there are many people who do not use the latrines that they own. Of course, because the 2011 census finds that 70 per cent of rural Indian households lack a latrine, open defecation in rural India is not, today, primarily caused by people failing to use the latrines that they own. It is caused by a great many people who could afford to own and use latrines choosing not to. But the fact that many people who own toilets do not use them nevertheless has two significant implications.

First, this fact has a practical implication for policymakers: A programme of toilet construction like the ones that the government has sponsored for decades will not be enough to end open defecation. Indeed, the SQUAT data projected that even if the government could overcome implementation constraints and corruption, and succeed in building a latrine for every household in the four focus states of the SQUAT survey, a majority of the people in those states would still perhaps defecate in the open.

Second, understanding how many people defecate in the open despite latrine ownership underscores just how low demand for latrine use really is in rural India. On their way to defecate in the fields each morning, many men and women walk right past a working latrine that is better than any latrine that the Bangladeshi labourer we met at the beginning of this chapter has ever used.

Such behaviour presents a puzzle. We certainly did not understand it when we first started assembling its pieces. In the next two chapters, we will turn to the question that we expect is now on your mind: *why?*

3 | Purity, pollution and untouchability

Three imposing mud pillars support the high ceiling of Ritesh Mishra's gateway. Most people who visit him stop there: In conservative Brahmin households like his, the inside space is reserved for women. But if you stopped at the impressive exterior, you would not know that the house is cramped on the inside. The interior offers only a small, open space for cooking at the front, with another small covered space for women to sleep at the back. The rest of the building belongs to Ritesh's extended family members, whose house is separated from his by an interior wall.

In the far corner of the entrance, a shelf is carved out of the thick mud wall. Beneath it, Ritesh sat cross-legged on a cot, his cheek bulging, and his lips stained red from the paan he was chewing. Nikhil and Diane approached him and Nikhil explained that they had come to this village in western Uttar Pradesh to learn about open defecation and latrine use in villages – would Ritesh be willing to talk for an hour or so?

Diane and Nikhil learnt that Ritesh and his wife are both in their forties. They live with their two unmarried children: a boy in his early twenties and an eighteen-year-old girl. All four family members defecate in the open. Ritesh goes to defecate twice a day, first around five in the morning and then again at seven at night. Each time he walks for about half an hour and goes to a different field or open space depending on his whim that day. His wife leaves to defecate earlier in the morning than he does, around four thirty, and returns to the house quickly to begin the day's work.

Ritesh explained that there had recently been a government latrine construction drive in the village, and that he had been offered a free latrine by the pradhan, or elected village leader. 'The pradhan wanted to give me a latrine, but I didn't take it … I didn't take it because [I'd have to pass by it on my way in and out, that would be awful]. There's not so much space either, and you can see that Lord Shiva's temple is there, and so is Barham baba's place. So, if I get a latrine built there, I would not like it …'

It was not entirely clear to us at the time what Ritesh would not like about a latrine being built by the temple. Nikhil wondered aloud whether Ritesh could have simply had the latrine built inside the house instead. 'What would be the problem with building a latrine inside the house?'

'What should I say to you, brother,' Ritesh answered. 'My heart doesn't allow for this. If one has [a latrine] in the house, it is quite disgusting. I do not like this. You can see that my house is [made of inexpensive materials], but you can also see that it is nicely coated with mud and cow-dung paste. Isn't it? So, in this way, we are people who live in a clean and healthy place. [Having a latrine] would make me feel disgusting. It smells, it smells like filth, that's why I wouldn't like it, brother. I was getting [a latrine for free], but I didn't take it.'

Why did Ritesh Mishra refuse the free latrine? In this chapter and in the next, we will try to explain a world view in which open defecation is clean and latrines are dirty. In order to do so, we will draw on others' research on the sociology and anthropology of rural India and also on our own field research. The SQUAT survey produced useful statistics, but to understand the puzzle of open defecation in rural India, we would have to take a different approach – to listen and learn about how people think. So, along with our team at r.i.c.e. we conducted many in-depth, conversational interviews in villages in Haryana, Uttar Pradesh, Gujarat and southern Nepal. When we still had open questions, we followed up with less-structured fieldwork and observation in Uttar Pradesh, Bihar, Rajasthan and Tamil Nadu. Most of this book, most of our research and most of the world's open defecation are concentrated in rural north India. As always, our fieldwork will be most relevant to the northern Indian plains states that we have studied, although we have seen evidence that these interpretations hold for other parts of India too.

Villagers' concepts of purity and pollution play an important role in explaining why Ritesh, Shantanu and their neighbours reject the kinds of inexpensive latrines that are used in other developing countries. Such concepts are intimately related to the Hindu caste system and to the struggle of untouchables to be accepted as equals.

Clean and dirty, pure and polluting, physical and ritual

In order to understand why Ritesh Mishra refused the latrine offered by the pradhan, we have to understand how he thinks about cleanliness and dirtiness. Ritesh is like people in many other societies in that it would be difficult for him to separate his concepts of cleanliness and dirtiness from his ideas about what is good and bad in a ritual, or a religious, sense. To make discussions of physical and ritual ideas clearer, sociologists and anthropologists often use the words 'pure' and 'purity' to talk about ritual or religious cleanliness, and 'impure' and 'pollution' to talk about ritual dirtiness. We will use these terms in that sense too.

How does a higher-caste Hindu in a village in north India conceive of cleanliness, dirtiness, purity and pollution? That was the question that R.S. Khare, then an anthropology PhD candidate at the University of Lucknow, set out to answer in a paper published in the *Eastern Anthropologist* in the early 1960s. Khare was particularly concerned with how people thought about the cleanliness and purity of their homes and daily lives.

Khare explains that, according to the villagers he studied, cleanliness and purity apply to objects, to situations and also to people. Physical cleanliness is not always the same as ritual cleanliness, although they can certainly overlap. Some objects are both ritually polluting and physically dirty, such as human faeces and used menstrual cloths. Some objects are physically clean, but nevertheless ritually polluting, like a drain which has just been cleaned out that removes waste water from the house. Vegetable peels strewn on the floor or rat excreta in flour are both seen as physically dirty but not ritually polluting. Over fifty years later, we meet many people in rural Uttar Pradesh who approach dirtiness and pollution in ways similar to those R.S. Khare documented in the 1960s.

Some of the objects and situations that villagers consider pure and impure would surprise people who did not grow up with this world view. For instance, many people in rural India, particularly Hindus, believe that cow dung and cow urine are purifying. In parts of rural India, and especially in Uttar Pradesh, houses are often made out of cow dung and mud. Women devote considerable time and energy before major religious holidays in applying a fresh layer of this mixture to the walls and floors. Cow urine and clarified butter are often used together in prayer and religious ceremonies.

In contrast, childbirth, newborn babies (even if clean) and mothers who have recently delivered babies are considered temporarily polluting to others. In some households, mother and child are isolated in a separate room. Visitors often bathe after visiting a newborn's house. Similarly, a ceremony held for children around their second birthday includes shaving their heads, because people believe that the hair that a child had in the womb is impure.

It would not always be obvious to someone who did not grow up in an Indian village which things people consider pure, which things they consider polluting and how one can avoid ritual pollution. But as M.N. Srinivas, an Indian sociologist, explains in *The Remembered Village*, children are taught to live by the rules of purity and pollution from a very young age. In the village in Karnataka where Srinivas did this fieldwork, Brahmin children as young as two years old were told to avoid touching lower-caste people. In Uttar Pradesh, Diane often watched parents hit the hands of babies who try to feed themselves with their left hand, which is considered polluting because it is used to clean oneself after defecation. This is enforced even though the hands of young children, cared for as they are by their mothers, have never actually been used for this purpose.

It is easy to be misled by the fact that ritual impurity is often described in the language of physical dirtiness. Ritesh said that latrines 'smell'. We hear this claim often, especially from people in cities who have used indoor flush toilets their entire lives. But physical smell is an absurd explanation for why open defecation is more common in India than in other developing countries – faeces are no more foul-smelling in India than elsewhere.

To be sure, even properly maintained rural latrines are not as pleasant as flushing, indoor toilets. Yet, we have used them on several continents and we can personally confirm that the smells they contain are perfectly consistent with the variation of smells found in village life. So, when somebody like Ritesh talks about smell in this context, he is referring to ritual impurity.

As R.S. Khare notes, villagers are often far more concerned with maintaining *ritual* purity than with maintaining those aspects of physical cleanliness that correspond with the germ theory of disease. As Ritesh's story suggests, it is also more important to people to maintain the cleanliness and purity of their own homes than it is to maintain the cleanliness and purity of public spaces. These views combine to work against the use of household latrines.

Pure people, less pure people and polluting people

Part of what make the concepts of purity and pollution so important for understanding life in India is that they are core concepts of the caste system. Caste is a complicated topic. It is central to many aspects of people's economic, social and family lives in both rural and urban India. Here, we can present only a basic discussion of caste, focusing on the parts that matter for rural open defecation.

A person's caste has many consequences for everyday life. It is inherited from one's parents at birth and cannot be changed. Among other things, one's caste influences whom one associates with, how one treats and is treated by other people and what kinds of jobs one does. It nearly always governs whom one will marry. Often, but not always, a person's surname indicates his caste. Caste is so important to the people in rural Uttar Pradesh that Diane is often asked her caste within minutes after meeting a new person.

There are ways in which caste is similar to systems of dividing and ranking people that exist in other societies, such as race in the US, South Africa or Latin America. Yet, there are also ways in which caste in South Asia is a unique social institution. Ideas about purity and pollution are often used to justify why some castes are ranked higher than others. People from higher castes are thought to be inherently more pure than people from lower castes, and they often try to behave in ways that reinforce this idea. Much has been written about the elaborate rituals that some Brahmins and members of other higher castes perform to assert and maintain their purity (and therefore superiority) over other people from other castes.

In addition to believing that objects (such as faeces and drains) and situations (such as death and childbirth) can affect the purity of a person who interacts with them, many higher-caste people also believe that people from the lower castes are polluting. In order to protect themselves from pollution by lower-caste people, higher-caste villagers often refuse food cooked by a lower-caste person, and will not sit with them at a festival, share a hookah with them or allow lower-caste people to enter their homes except to do menial work. In some situations, lower-caste people are believed to pollute higher-caste people, but in other situations they are required to absorb or clean up pollution that might befall a higher-caste person, in order to make him or her pure again. Indeed, when Diane and her research assistant, Baby, were studying a government programme to promote hospital birth in rural Uttar Pradesh, one thing that families talked about was the need to hire women from untouchable castes to 'clean up' the pollution associated with childbirth.

A higher-caste Muslim mother-in-law named Fatima told us that even if her daughter-in-law gave birth at the hospital, and even if they threw out her bloodstained petticoat at the hospital, they would still have to hire someone from the Dhobi caste to wash the clothing that her daughter-in-law used at the hospital. Knowing that Fatima's daughter and daughter-in-law typically wash the family's clothes by hand, like almost every other family in the village, Diane asked why they would bother to pay a Dhobi in this case. Fatima explained, 'We still have to call the Dhobi, so that other people see this.'

It is not that Dhobi women get clothes physically cleaner than Fatima would. Instead, they absorb the pollution of childbirth in a public way so that Fatima's daughter-in-law – indeed, the whole family – can be absolved of the ritual impurity of childbirth. If higher-caste people do not follow purity and pollution rules like this one, they are likely to suffer important social consequences. In the next chapter, we will focus on the social consequences of an extreme case of breaking purity and pollution norms: The work of emptying latrine pit that is eventually required by the adoption of pit latrines.

Fatima's house and family could be purified after the birth of a child by the passage of time and by employing a lower-caste person. In contrast, there are some people who, by virtue of their caste, are seen as permanently polluted and polluting to others. People from the lowest castes have often been considered to be so polluting to members of higher castes that they, subjectively, could not be touched. Hence the English word for this group: 'untouchable'. Throughout the book, we use the word Dalit to describe people from these castes because Dalit, which means 'oppressed' or, literally, 'broken into pieces', captures Dalits' past and present struggles for survival and equality.

We have heard some urbanites claim that discrimination against Dalits was part of India's past, but is no longer practised today. This is not true. A large fraction of people in urban

India admit to practising untouchability. Economists Amit Thorat and Omkar Joshi analysed survey responses from the nationally representative 2012 India Human Development Survey (IHDS) and found that about 20 per cent of urban respondents report having at least one family member who practises untouchability.

An even higher fraction of *rural* respondents in the IHDS survey report that at least one family member practises untouchability. We ourselves have encountered many different untouchability practices in our fieldwork in rural Sitapur. Diane remembers when Saroj, a young woman whom she was interviewing, initially refused to give her a glass of water on a hot day. Saroj was washing dishes at the time and had both clean water and a clean glass within reach. But when Diane asked for the water, she paused and eventually said that she belonged to a Dalit caste. Saroj was concerned that Diane could become angry if she unknowingly accepted water from a Dalit. Diane explained that she does not believe in untouchability and does not have a caste herself. Surprised, and perhaps somewhat suspicious, Saroj eventually handed over a glass of water.

Dirty people, dirty work and dirty spaces

Rules about purity and pollution are often used to reinforce caste hierarchies. This is especially common when higher-caste people interact with Dalits. If you ask a villager from a middle or higher caste why Dalits are treated so poorly, he might say that it is because they do 'dirty' – by which he also means 'polluting' – work.

It is true that much of the work traditionally performed by Dalits – including removing animal carcasses from the village, cleaning faeces and trash from public places, preparing dead bodies for cremation – is physically dirty. However, some of the work that Dalits traditionally do, such as drumming or crafting shoes out of leather, would not be considered physically dirty by someone who does not endorse the caste system. Similar to the case of a recently cleaned household drain, the 'dirtiness' of these jobs is ritual dirtiness, rather than physical dirtiness. Anthropologist Sarah Pinto points out that the logic behind people's thinking about caste and cleanliness is circular: Dalits are dirty because they perform dirty jobs, and the jobs are dirty because Dalits perform them.

There are some people – typically conservative members of the higher castes – who claim that avoiding contact with people who do 'dirty' jobs, or observing other purity and pollution rules, such as not sharing food or water, functionally serves to promote hygiene and health. These rules are not, however, based on the germ theory of disease; in fact, they long pre-date it. Purity and pollution rules have little to do with germs and much to do with enforcing subordination of lower-caste people. Indeed, some behaviours that enforce subordination of the lower castes end up creating serious hygiene problems.

We will soon see how rural open defecation is related to the oppression of lower-caste people in Indian villages. Caste identity and the subordination of Dalits also matter for the cleanliness of public spaces more broadly.

Sociologist Damaris Lüthi has studied hygiene behaviour in Kottar, a small city in Tamil Nadu. She describes how, in a Hindu value system, the cleanliness and purity of the home are very important. The purity of the home is seen as a reflection of one's character and status: Many purity rules focus on the home. However, Lüthi observes, interest in cleanliness stops 'at the doorsteps of private homes, and habits related to the outside define it as an irrelevant rubbish dump'.

Anand Teltumbde, a professor of management at IIT Kharagpur and scholar of Dalit movements, explains in *Economic and Political Weekly* that the litter problem plaguing Indian cities is not only about people not caring what happens to public spaces but also about caste politics. Indians throw their trash on the ground not merely out of laziness but also to assert their superiority over Dalits. It is, after all, Dalits who are expected to clean public places.

When the Swachh Bharat Mission was launched in 2014, signs appeared in metropolitan public spaces, especially in upmarket areas, urging citizens to dispose of trash in trash cans as an act of civic pride. Teltumbde's work suggests that cleaning up urban India will require not only a new sense of civic responsibility but also a change in the attitudes of higher-caste people towards Dalits. However, such a shift may also require Dalits and members of other lower castes to reject higher-caste values. Such a thing is easy to write about, but extremely difficult to do in Saroj's world – where even handing a glass of water to a visitor of unknown caste rank could have serious social consequences.

Getting ahead where some people are pure and some people are polluting

Different states, even different villages, have different rules that govern caste interactions and purity and pollution. Even within a village, not everyone always agrees on the exact rank order among a group of castes. One way that members of one caste may try to assert their superiority over another is by adopting more stringent purity and pollution restrictions.

For instance, members of upwardly mobile castes often adopt dietary practices that are seen as pure, such as vegetarianism and avoiding alcohol. M.N. Srinivas famously termed this process 'sanskritization'.

The adoption of higher-caste values and practices by members of the middle and lower castes is widely considered by sociologists of India to be a major force of cultural change in India. For the urban elites who do not travel further than the new Dunkin' Donuts or Subway restaurants dotting the posh markets of Delhi and Mumbai, it is easy to forget that, for members of lower and Dalit castes in Indian villages, upward social mobility often means adopting the practices and beliefs of their locally powerful neighbours rather than adopting Western practices and beliefs.

Efforts by members of the lower castes to disassociate themselves from their stigmatized caste identities often involve rejecting practices that are frowned upon by the higher castes, even if those practices are beneficial, practical or meaningful to them. For example, in the opening pages of his autobiography, Om Prakash Valmiki, a Dalit raised in Uttar Pradesh, wrote about how the upwardly mobile Dalits in his village slowly stopped raising pigs:

> Pigs were an important part of our lives. In sickness or in health, in life or in death, in wedding ceremonies – pigs played an important role in all of them. Even our religious ceremonies were incomplete without the pigs. The pigs rooting in the compound were not symbols of dirt to us but of prosperity, and so they are today. Yet, the educated among us, who are still a minute percentage, have abandoned these conventions. It is not because of a reformist perspective but because of their inferiority

complex that they have done so. The educated ones suffer more from this inferiority complex, which is caused by social pressures.

Valmiki's observation that educated Dalits in Uttar Pradesh gave up raising pigs is important for our story because it shows that abandoning traditional Dalit practices is an important way in which Dalits in rural India have tried to change their social position – even at a meaningful economic cost. In the next chapter, we will explore another strategy that Dalits use to challenge an oppressive social order: abandoning 'dirty work', such as emptying latrine pits, even if such work would be economically profitable.

What do purity, pollution and untouchability have to do with open defecation?

We now turn back to the question of why India has such uniquely high rates of open defecation. We are not the only ones to raise the idea that public filth may be connected to ritual pollution. For example, when the *Hindustan Times* asked Delhi University sociologist André Béteille, in the summer of 2016, why the Swachh Bharat Mission did not seem to be succeeding, he explained, 'In our obsession for ritual purity, we make compromises with physical cleanliness.'

When Ritesh Mishra told Diane and Nikhil that he likes to live in a 'clean sort of place', he was not merely saying that he likes his house to be swept and the dishes stacked neatly. He unmistakably meant ritual cleanliness, not physical cleanliness. He was explaining that, as a Brahmin, it is important to him to avoid those things that are considered polluting to higher-caste Hindus and to maintain a home and a body that his neighbours would recognize as ritually pure.

In our qualitative interviews, we heard similar claims from higher-caste villagers in other places too. In Haryana, a young Brahmin named Gaurav told us:

> If a latrine is in the house, there will be bad smells, germs will grow. Latrines in the house are like ... hell. The environment becomes completely polluted. There is no benefit of lighting [religious candles and lamps], no benefit at all.

Notably, Gaurav mixes claims based on the germ theory of disease with ideas about ritual purity. He had heard about how open defecation spreads germs and disease. But he was particularly concerned about the ritual pollution associated with defecating in the house. To Gaurav, the presence of faeces contained in a latrine at the house would be so *ritually polluting* as to require *ritual purification*, in the form of candles and lamps that are used in prayer. To him, not even these tools for ritual purification stand up to the pollution of having a latrine at the house.

Many higher-caste respondents were particularly concerned about having a latrine close to the kitchen. Aside from places of prayer, the kitchen is the place that is supposed to be kept most ritually pure. For instance, many people would be very upset if a Dalit person were to enter their kitchen.

In contrast to the higher-caste households, the lower-caste households that did not own latrines were far less likely to make explicit reference to ideas about ritual purity and pollution when explaining why they did not invest in latrines. This makes sense, considering that such ideas have long been used to justify their own oppression. But the lower-caste respondents still implicitly accepted and enacted these values by describing the dirtiness and smells that they associated with latrine use. This also makes sense: In a society where social mobility depends on adopting the value systems of the caste elite, why would lower-caste people set themselves apart as different and worse by installing a latrine, when the only benefit they see is, perhaps, convenience?

———

We have met many people who have helped us understand why latrine ownership and use are so low in rural India, despite the fact that most households are at least as rich as households in other developing countries that have much lower rates of open defecation. Gaurav and Ritesh Mishra have helped us see that ideas about purity and pollution, which are most strongly expressed and enforced by members of the higher castes, also describe their rejection of affordable latrines. Fatima and Saroj have helped us understand the importance of purity and pollution rules in everyday interactions in rural India. Valmiki and Srinivas have helped us see how sanskritization is a major force for caste mobility and cultural change, sometimes even at an economic cost. In the case of open defecation, this means that even members of lower castes are less concerned about having a more convenient place to defecate than they are about negotiating a higher social rank.

The fact that many rural Indians profess a preference for open defecation is not to say that villagers could not one day come to more strongly associate latrine use with convenience, as urbanites do, and as do many people in other developing countries. But it is important to note that the unique systems of purity, pollution, caste and social subordination that we have discussed in this chapter are real and important barriers to latrine adoption. They are rooted in India's cultural context and are not the same as whatever social norms may have formerly slowed latrine adoption in other parts of the world.

In the next chapter, we will look more carefully at the types of toilets households in rural India build when they invest in latrines. Alongside this investigation of latrine hardware, we will further explore the history of untouchability. This history, which is important for human well-being in ways that extend far beyond open defecation, blocks the kind of latrine technology that has played a major role in the reduction of open defecation everywhere else.

4 | Latrine pits and slow social change

Sohni Devi lives with her two small children and her mother-in-law in a Dalit hamlet on the edge of a large village in western Uttar Pradesh. Her husband, a migrant labourer who works on construction projects in large cities like Delhi, Mumbai and Kanpur, comes to the village occasionally.

Surrounded by her neighbours, who frequently contributed their own views to the interview, Sohni Devi agreed to talk with Diane and Nikhil about her life, her home and her latrine. She told us that her house was built by her mother- and father-in-law. It has two parts, one made of bricks and the other made of mud and cow dung. The room that is made of bricks was paid for by the government's Indira Awaas Yojana programme. The thatched roof often leaks and needs to be fixed frequently. The latrine in front of the house is too short for a tall adult to stand up in, but because one does not stand up in a latrine it is functional.

Diane and Nikhil quickly learnt that Sohni Devi and her husband did not build the latrine themselves. Instead, the pradhan, an elected village leader, had hired workers to build it for them three years ago. Sohni Devi and her husband had merely indicated the spot where it was to be built. The pradhan also built latrines for all the other families in the lower-caste hamlet.

Diane asked Sohni Devi whether she had ever thought of building a latrine before the pradhan built this one. She explained, 'Our house is broken and falling apart, why would we build a latrine?'

She does not use the latrine she has. She, her mother-in-law and her husband all defecate in the open. The two children, aged seven and five, use the latrine now, but the family will tear it down when the children are old enough to defecate in the open on their own.

To Diane and Nikhil, the latrine seemed convenient. And Sohni Devi herself admitted that it saves her the hassle of cleaning up the children's faeces. Her children, like the small children in other families in the village who do not own a latrine, would otherwise defecate in the area in front of the house.

Yet, as the conversation went on, it became increasingly clear that Sohni Devi was annoyed that the pradhan built a latrine on their land. Exasperated with the village government, she said, 'The pradhan made this [latrine]. If we'd made it, we'd have made it the way we wanted. All of this *Indira Vikas* money has come, so the pradhan has made it. But he only got a very little pit dug. If we made it the way we wanted, then wouldn't we have used a whole room full of bricks? How can a poor man? ... It costs twenty or twenty-five thousand rupees to [make a latrine].'

In Chapter 2, we saw that India's exceptionally high rates of open defecation cannot be explained by poverty, nor by illiteracy, nor by lack of water, nor by poor governance. The comparison of India's open defecation rates to those of other developing countries presented a puzzle.

Chapter 3 gave the first part of our two-part answer to this central question: Why do so many people in rural India defecate in the open? Although many societies have ideas about what is clean and dirty, rural Indians' ideas about purity and pollution are globally unique and are intimately related to the Hindu caste system. Chapter 3 explored the ways in which these ideas discourage latrine use and promote open defecation.

This chapter completes our answer to the question of why so many people in rural India defecate in the open. Here, we focus on untouchability, a social institution that is undeniably one of the darkest and most oppressive aspects of the Hindu caste system.* India's history of untouchability and the ways in which life is changing for Dalits mean that most households do not see using an affordable pit latrine as a viable option. As Sohni Devi explained, villagers subjectively understand their sanitation options to be one of two: Either build an expensive latrine with a cement-lined tank as large as a small house, or defecate in the open.

The toilets that save lives elsewhere

As we discussed in Chapter 2, the reason why there is little relationship between GDP or poverty and latrine-use across countries is that the latrines that can prevent the spread of infectious diseases are actually quite affordable. Many people in Bangladesh, for instance, build and use latrines that cost as little as 2,000 to 3,000 rupees. Most of these latrines use water seals to prevent bad smells and stop flies from coming in and

---

*   This chapter contains a few instances in which people we have interviewed refer to specific Dalit castes in terms that are considered objectionable and insulting. We share the view that these terms are insulting but have chosen to use exact quotations because they are important for understanding how people in rural India think about caste and sanitation.

out of the pit. Latrines in sub-Saharan Africa typically cost even less, although they are less likely to use water seals.

From a health perspective, the most important part of a rural latrine is the underground pit. The World Health Organization (WHO) promotes the use of inexpensive latrines that have underground pits that are about 1.5 cubic metres in volume. The WHO recommends that pits be lined with bricks or rocks laid in a 'honeycomb' pattern. This allows water to seep out of the pit into the ground so that eventually the only thing left to be stored in the pit is decomposing faeces, which are also largely water.

The latrines that are built under the Swachh Bharat Mission are much more expensive than WHO-recommended latrines. The former have brick-and-mortar *superstructures* above the ground, rather than less expensive superstructures made of tin, plastic, bamboo or cloth. However, the latrine *pits* recommended by the Indian government are similar in size to the ones that the WHO recommends. If they were built and used properly, government-recommended latrines would successfully interrupt the transmission of disease, saving lives and promoting child growth.

The WHO estimates that when a normal latrine (meaning one with a 1.5 cubic metres, honeycomb-style pit) is used daily by a family of six, it will fill up in about five years. When the pit fills up, the owners must either empty it or build a new pit. If the owners opt for emptying the pit, in rural parts of developing countries, the emptying is almost always done manually rather than with a machine.

Across rural India – from Gujarat to Bihar to Tamil Nadu – we searched for a family that had had their government or WHO-style latrine pit emptied with a machine. When we did not find one, we became curious about whether mechanical emptying of affordable latrine pits would be possible, even in principle.

To find out, we interviewed a sanitation worker in Tamil Nadu named Arokyaraj who owns and operates a sewage truck. Arokyaraj, a Dalit whose forefathers had converted to Christianity, typically uses his truck to empty large cement-lined tanks in the town where he lives. To do this, he lowers a hose into the tank and uses a vacuum to suck the wet sludge into a tank on his truck.

We asked Arokyaraj whether he had ever been hired to empty a latrine pit in a village. He explained that he occasionally empties tanks for wealthier rural households, but he has never emptied a honeycomb-style latrine pit with his machines. There are two reasons why he thought this would be impractical. One is that honeycomb-style latrine pits are designed for water to seep out, making the faeces in the pit hard and difficult to extract with a vacuum. Arokyaraj said he would have to pump water into the pit to soften the hardened faeces before extracting them, which would be messy and would cause him to interact more closely with the sludge. The second reason is that vacuum extraction and disposal of sludge is expensive, so it would not be cost-effective for someone to hire him to dispose of sludge in such small quantities.

After talking with Arokyaraj, we understood better why none of the households we met thought mechanical emptying of latrine pits was a plausible option. In rural India, as in other parts of the developing world, when honeycomb-style latrine pits are emptied, it is done by hand.

However, emptying pits manually can be hazardous to the health of the emptier if the job is done too soon after the pit fills up. The government and the WHO recommend that a pit be left unused for several months after it fills up (depending on the soil type) so that the faeces decompose. A full latrine pit will decompose after about six months. Decomposed faeces are safer to handle than fresh sludge. They will not transmit bacterial and viral infections. This means that each latrine needs two pits. People who already have a latrine can continue to use the same superstructure, but direct their faeces to a second pit while the first decomposes.

The vast majority of people we interviewed in rural India did not know that letting faeces decompose makes it safer to empty a latrine pit by hand. When we explained this, people very often reacted with scepticism. As we will explain below, biological germs are not the barrier to emptying of pits. People in rural India equate manually emptying a latrine pit with the most degrading forms of Dalit labour. Therefore, the idea of manually emptying a latrine pit is at least as reviled for its social implications as it is for the physically disgusting nature of the work.

In writing about the ways in which faecal sludge from pit latrines would ideally be managed in low-income countries, we do not mean to imply that in countries other than India faecal sludge is managed well. Unfortunately, proper pit-emptying practices are often not followed in many developing countries. We have read many accounts from sub-Saharan Africa and parts of South Asia outside of India in which people empty fresh sludge by hand and dispose of it in rivers or other places where the germs can infect others. Our point is simply to explain that sanitation options that exist in other countries are also, in principle, options for India: Pit latrines could be used and emptied, in perhaps imperfect ways, which would nevertheless improve health considerably. International data shows that even imperfect management of faecal sludge would reduce children's exposure to faecal germs. For example, we will see in the next chapter that developing countries with less open defecation have better health outcomes including taller children, even though faecal sludge is not perfectly managed in any of them.

The toilets that rural Indians build

Even though sanitation officials in the Indian government have known for decades that inexpensive latrines with two pits would substantially improve health in villages, and despite the promotion of this technology by some high-profile sanitation NGOs, the adoption of such latrines is extremely limited. The SQUAT survey found that only 2.5 per cent of households with a latrine were using a twin-pit model. It also found that even though the government promotes twin-pit latrines on paper, there is little on-the-ground effort to teach people about the twin-pit design. As a result, the twin-pit latrines that exist are often constructed incorrectly, such as with the pits connected by pipes underground.

As Sohni Devi's story suggests, part of the reason why the government fails to get people to use affordable twin-pit latrines is that government latrines are very different from the latrines that rural Indians build for themselves. For one thing, the latrines that people build for themselves are much more expensive. Sohni Devi's estimate of 20,000 to 25,000 rupees is very close to what SQUAT survey respondents in rural north India said was the cost of a minimally acceptable latrine. In fact, when male SQUAT survey respondents were asked to describe, part by part, what an inexpensive but usable latrine would look like, they described a latrine that cost, on average, 21,000 rupees.

How does the price of a latrine get from 2,000 rupees in Bangladesh to 21,000 rupees in India? The first step-up in price, from 2,000 rupees to 12,000 rupees, is the step from internationally normal latrines to Indian government latrines. This step happens above ground, in the construction of the superstructure. The second step-up in price, from 12,000 rupees to 21,000 rupees, happens below ground. The major difference between the 21,000-rupee latrine described by Sohni Devi and the SQUAT survey respondents and the 12,000-rupee latrine that the government promotes under the Swachh Bharat Mission lies in the size of the underground pit.

Many poor families in rural India live in just one room. Families that live in brick rooms are typically better off than those who live in rooms made out of mud and dung. When Sohni Devi first told us that building a latrine pit is like building a room, which in her context would amount to a house, we thought she must be exaggerating. Shortly thereafter, we came across a wealthy family that was in the process of constructing a latrine in front of their house. The pit was even larger than what Sohni Devi had described! The family told us that the pit measured 3 metres × 3 metres × 3 metres. Sohni Devi was right: The bricks that were used to construct such a large latrine pit could have been used to more than double the size of the single room that her in-laws had built so many years before.

Once we learnt that large pits were responsible for the high prices that people paid for latrines, we asked to see latrines that were under construction in many of the villages we visited. In other states, including Gujarat, Tamil Nadu and Rajasthan, we came across many other enormous pits. Among SQUAT survey respondents, we found that the median size of a privately constructed latrine pit was about 7 cubic metres – nearly five times as large as the WHO recommends! In our interviews, many people told us that they aspire to own pits even larger than that.

Missing middle rungs on the sanitation ladder

International sanitation professionals often use the analogy of a ladder to explain the different types of latrines in developing countries. Successive rungs on the ladder represent more hygienic options – which can be more expensive but need not be very much so. The lowest rung represents open defecation. Higher rungs progress to the simplest pit latrines (without a water seal), to pour-flush pit latrines with a water seal, to private toilets that connect to a septic tank or a sewer.

The sanitation ladder in India is missing its middle rungs, with no intermediate steps on which households climb gradually up from open defecation towards flush toilets. The annual WHO and UNICEF Joint Monitoring Report gives the fraction of households in each developing country and region that use inexpensive, unimproved latrines. In countries that the WHO and UNICEF define as 'low income', over 40 per cent of households use unimproved latrines, but in India, only 15 per cent of households, including urban households, use this missing middle sanitation option. In the poorest of the low income countries, the fraction of households using unimproved facilities is even higher. In Malawi, for instance, more than 80 per cent of households use unimproved sanitation, but only 7 per cent defecate in the open.

The Census of India 2011 similarly found that Indians either defecate in the open or use the most expensive sanitation options. Census data separates sanitation options into 'water closets', 'pit latrines' and 'other latrines'. Nearly 80 per cent of the households using any sort of toilet or latrine use water closets, which are the most expensive option included in the questionnaire.

Why do rural Indians want such expensive toilets that sit atop large pits? Why do they reject the affordable options that are found in other developing countries? In short, why do rural Indians reject government pit latrines? Answering these questions requires an understanding of rural India's history of untouchability, and particularly the practice of manual scavenging.

Manual scavenging

Manual scavenging, in which people interact with and dispose of human faeces by hand, is a type of Dalit labour that is particularly relevant to India's open defecation problem. Although jobs involving manual scavenging have become considerably less common than they once were in rural India, there are still places where manual scavengers are employed to clean what are misleadingly named 'dry latrines'. Dry latrines are areas in or around the home where people defecate on a concrete slab or on the open ground. Manual scavengers collect faeces in baskets and dispose of them outside the village or neighbourhood.

Manual scavenging is considered even more degrading and humiliating than the kinds of rural Dalit labour we discussed in Chapter 3. In fact, it is considered so degrading that it is difficult to interview the relatively small number of people who do this work today without embedding oneself in a village for a long period of time. Further, many villages no longer have any residents who would do manual scavenging even if they were paid well for it. However, older people from castes that once did manual scavenging sometimes agree to talk about it. One of them is Prakash.

Prakash belongs to the Valmiki caste and lives in a village with his wife, daughter and extended family members; his two sons live outside the village. The younger son is studying in Lucknow and the older son is preparing for the admissions tests for an engineering degree. While he is preparing for the tests, the older son lives and works at the Delhi headquarters of an Uttar Pradesh–based political party. Despite the fact that he has passed class twelve, Prakash's son works as a cleaner in the office.

Prakash explained to Nikhil what it was like to work as a manual scavenger. He said, 'People used to construct spaces for women to squat by putting bricks or slabs on the ground. And then the servants, the scavengers, used to come and spread ashes on the faeces and then take them away by collecting them in a basket using a tin plate.'

His wife, who was listening to the conversation, shared her experiences too – manual scavenging was most often women's work. They told Nikhil that some people would tell the manual scavengers to collect the faeces that they removed in pits so that the contents of the pits could later be used as manure. Manual scavengers were then hired to spread the manure on the fields after it had decomposed.

Manual scavenging often causes the people who do it to be physically nauseated and to be sick with skin, intestinal and other diseases. Handling faeces is even worse when it is hot or raining outside than when the weather is cold and dry.

Fortunately, census data suggests that the fraction of households that employ manual scavengers has declined considerably in the last thirty years. Many higher-caste and Muslim households that kept women in purdah used to employ manual scavengers to clean dry latrines. In recent years, many of these households have either built expensive latrines or have started allowing women to defecate in the open.

However, manual scavenging has by no means been eliminated. Many forms of manual scavenging are still common, even in urban settings. It is not known exactly how many people still use dry latrines or how many people are employed to clean them. The 2011 census found that about 800,000 households across the country reported using dry latrines. This figure is perhaps an underestimate of the actual use of dry latrine. For reasons we describe below, census respondents may hesitate to report the use of a dry latrine to someone filling in a government survey.

In 1993, Parliament passed a law that made it illegal to hire manual scavengers in several states of India. In 2013, the law – called the Prohibition of Employment as Manual Scavengers and their Rehabilitation Act – was updated to cover the entire country. In principle, it imposes a fine and a potential prison sentence on people who employ manual scavengers. In addition to cleaning dry latrines, it identifies several other activities as manual scavenging as well. For example, hiring someone to handle human faeces, without protective gear, in a drain, latrine pit, sewer, public toilet or railway track, is legally considered manual scavenging. It is important to note, though, that the act *does not* prohibit hiring someone to empty a twin-pit latrine in which faeces have decomposed.

The fact that the act prohibiting manual scavenging exists represents an important accomplishment of decades of advocacy for social equality. Indeed, an essay by Ambedkar titled 'The Revolt of the Untouchables' reminds us that the laws of British India used to make it a punishable offence for members of scavenging castes to *refuse* to do manual scavenging work.

However, despite the valuable signal that the act prohibiting manual scavenging sends, the government's commitment to enforcing the act has been weak. We could find no evidence that the government has ever convicted anyone under either of the acts of 1993 and 2013. Several newspapers report that no one was ever convicted for employing manual scavengers during the twenty-year period from 1993 to 2013. Further, the National Crime Records Bureau, which publishes the number of cases registered for each crime for each year, listed no registered cases under the act for any state in 2014.

The lack of convictions should not be misinterpreted as evidence that manual scavenging has been eliminated; it still exists. Some 800,000 households openly admitted to using dry latrines in the 2011 census. Activists such as Bezwada Wilson and his colleagues at the Safai Karmachari Andolan, as well as other organizations against manual scavenging, have brought many cases of manual scavenging to the attention of government officials without securing prosecutions.

Even if the government is not willing to prosecute people for employing manual scavengers, there are many other ways it could work to bring an end to manual scavenging. In urban India, many different forms of manual scavenging take place in plain sight. As a matter of course, the Indian state actually hires people to do manual scavenging in the drains and sewers of cities. Many people have died as a result of this dangerous work.

To reduce manual scavenging in cities, large public investments in infrastructure are needed to update railway coaches and city sewage systems – alongside better regulation of mechanical sewage removal for urban households that are not connected to sewers. These investments are feasible and would be well worth it. They would help the government comply with its own law to promote the health and dignity of sanitation workers. These investments would be a visible, public stand against caste discrimination. They would also work against the disastrous consequences of poor sanitation for health and the economy that we will investigate in the coming chapters, if only because less casteism may eventually translate into less open defecation.

If the government wants to end manual scavenging and promote latrine use, it should do a great deal more to inform the public about the 2013 act. Many people we talked with in rural north India knew that hiring manual scavengers is no longer socially acceptable, but did not know that it is illegal. There are even people, especially from manual scavenging castes, who told us they thought that it was illegal to *perform* manual scavenging, rather than to *hire* manual scavengers.

Life in the lowest castes

By the end of this chapter, we aim to explain what untouchability and manual scavenging have to do with the absence of affordable latrines, and therefore with rural India's open defecation crisis. But in order to understand what it means to be a manual scavenger in rural India, it is not enough to understand how physically disgusting the work would be. One must also understand the extreme exploitation, exclusion and humiliation that people from the Dalit castes have faced for generations. Here, we can paint a picture of life in the lowest castes only in broad brushstrokes, but it bears emphasis that manual scavengers are considered the lowest-ranking among the Dalit castes. The discrimination they face is generally even worse than that which Dalits from non-scavenging castes face.

In *The Annihilation of Caste*, Ambedkar catalogues a few of the particular ways in which Dalits were prevented from participating in essential parts of village life. In many villages, Dalits were prohibited from drawing water from common wells and other water sources. This practice did not end at the time of Independence. In his 1976 ethnography of a village in Karnataka, M.N. Srinivas explains that Dalits 'were ... excluded from using the big tank, and only the canals taking off from it were permitted to them. It was all right for water to flow from the higher castes to Harijans, but not the other way about.' Further, Dalits were commonly prohibited from entering temples and were even sometimes prevented from attending government schools.

Ambedkar also discusses some of the common untouchability practices intended to humiliate Dalits. He writes that in some places in Maharashtra, Dalits were required to wear black threads so that non-Dalits could avoid contact with them, and thereby avoid becoming polluted. In Jaipur, Dalits were assaulted by caste Hindus for eating ghee at a festival, on the grounds that ghee was a delicacy reserved for higher-caste people.

Dalit writer Om Prakash Valmiki, whom we met in Chapter 3, called his autobiography *Joothan*, after the scraps of food that Dalits ate off discarded leaf plates at weddings. In a public display of subservience and humiliation, Dalits were expected to clean up after a wedding had taken place in the village. They would pick up the leaf plates that had been thrown on the ground, eat the scraps left on the plates and dispose of them outside the village.

These are only a few examples of the suffering to which people from the Dalit castes have been subjected for generations. There are no doubt many, many others that have not been written about. The point that we intend to make in discussing them is that untouchability is about far more than the physical unpleasantness of performing certain kinds of work. It is about a social and economic system that exploits, excludes and humiliates some people and privileges others.

Resistance and social change

Thankfully, research suggests that rural untouchability practices have changed in recent decades. Based on fieldwork in eleven states and 565 villages, researchers Ghanshyam Shah, Harsh Mander, Sukhadeo Thorat, Satish Deshpande and Amita

Baviskar found that even though discrimination against Dalits continues to be widespread in rural India, many of the most extreme untouchability practices, such as preventing Dalits from walking on roads or from using public transportation, have declined considerably.

The stories that we have been told by older Dalits in villages in Uttar Pradesh are consistent with this research. For instance, Prakash, who described manual scavenging in an interview with Nikhil, explained that the practice of forcing Dalits to eat joothan is something that ended in his lifetime:

> I have seen [Dalits clean up and eat scraps at weddings] but ever since I became an adult, we have not done joothan work. I'll tell you that I certainly won't eat anyone else's joothan. I will work, and in exchange, I should be paid something, but it won't be enough just to give me leftover food. In my parents' time, they had to take joothan, but in my time that practice has ended.

Day-to-day economic relationships between Dalits and higher-caste villagers have changed as well. Nikhil interviewed an older Dalit woman named Nandini and her husband Dayaram, whose relatives have worked for landowning Thakurs in their village for several generations. Nandini still does housework in a Thakur home. They described a time when they had less choice about whether to work for the Thakurs, and when higher-caste landowners did not permit Dalits to sit on cots or wear clean clothes in their presence. Nandini recalled:

> In earlier days people were terrorized by the landowners, but now it has changed. Now, if you want you can work for them, and if you don't want to they can't do anything.

If we were in the old times, you could not have sat on the cot if he [the landowner] was walking near you. You could not sit if he was there. If you sat or wore nice clothes in front of him, he would feel offended. But now he can't do anything, the time of his rule has ended.

Nandini explained that working for the landowners is markedly different from what it once was – they now pay her money in addition to food, and she feels free to stop working for them if she wants. But ways continue to be there in which they humiliate her. Sometimes the women in the family she works for sprinkle water in the places where she walks to make the spot where she walked ritually pure again. Nandini says that the Thakurs would still never share a meal or their dishes with her.

How did these changes in the ways Dalits are treated come about? As in the explanations of many large social changes, there have been many contributing factors. As the economy became more monetized and transportation improved, Dalits had the option to leave villages and move to cities. Government policies have also helped. Ambedkar fought for and achieved affirmative action policies for Dalits that are written into the Indian Constitution. We hope laws like the acts of 1993 and 2013 against manual scavenging the anti-untouchability act of 1955 and the anti-atrocities act of 1989 make an expressive difference even if the government implements them poorly. And perhaps most importantly, Dalits have resisted their own exploitation, exclusion and humiliation in ways that chip away at the system that discriminates against them.

Near our home in rural Sitapur, we saw some examples of things changing for the better. Neha, a young Valmiki woman we know, refuses to clean drains around others' homes in the way that her mother does and that her older sister did before she got married. Her family does not insist Neha do the work because her father has a stable income as a government safai karmachari. In this case, economic progress contributes to social progress, reinforcing a low-ranking woman's decision to choose for herself.

Nikhil and Sangita met an older Dalit woman who only recently decided to challenge the village norm that she was not allowed to enter the temple. She explained how she finally decided to go to the temple, and what happened afterwards:

> There is a temple over that way, but we [Dalits] didn't go to it. Then some people started saying that the [statue of a cow] was drinking water – the cow was drinking water! So, I thought: 'I'm going to go to the temple to see that!' I thought I would go and see that cow … I also thought that I would find out whether anyone would say anything to me for going into the temple. And if they did, I was ready to fight … if someone came to my house to [say something about it] then I would run him off like I were an angry dog. So, then when I went and offered water to the cow statue, no one said anything to me! They didn't say anything, and I didn't say anything. I thought it was a very good thing! Now, after that day, I go to the temple.

Although the social changes that are taking place in villages are encouraging, manual scavenging, untouchability and discrimination nevertheless continue. In many villages and towns, Dalits live in enclaves that are poorer and have worse services than higher-caste neighbourhoods. Across the country, daily news stories document violence against Dalits, including rapes, assaults and indignities, such as when Dalits are attacked for holding wedding processions that were traditionally reserved for higher castes.

Another important limit on social change is that higher castes have not been willing to start doing work that is considered dirty or polluting. This fact brings us back to sanitation: There are limits to the social and sanitary progress that can be made when higher-caste people will not remove their own dead animal carcasses, unblock their own drains, cut their own babies' umbilical cords and, most importantly for our puzzle, empty their own latrine pits.

Untouchability and emptying the latrine pit

In other developing countries, where untouchability and manual scavenging never existed, emptying latrine pits is a job done by people who are poor and down on their luck. But they are not people whose parents were prevented from drawing water from a well. They are not people whose parents were forced to eat scraps after public functions. In other countries, emptying latrine pits is an unpleasant job rather than a symbol of generations of oppression and humiliation. India's history of untouchability – and the way it is being renegotiated in villages today – is what makes the job of emptying latrine pits in Indian villages markedly different from other places in the developing world.

If higher-caste people cannot look beyond the supposedly polluting nature of sanitation work and learn to see the people who do such work as equals, it may help to accelerate social progress if more people like Neha refuse to do the stigmatizing work that others expect of them. This is a strategy that many Dalit activists have promoted, even as other Dalits advocate instead for better pay and working conditions – especially those like Neha's father, who have found meagre economic security in performing untouchable work.

It is against this backdrop that people in villages fret about what will happen if they were to use a simple pit latrine, and if that pit were to fill up.

───

By the time we had finished the SQUAT survey and the qualitative study that we describe in Notes at the end of this book, our whole team had come to understand how important the lack of affordable pit latrines is to India's open defecation crisis. But we did not yet fully understand just how difficult it would be to get a latrine pit emptied in a village. Could someone get a latrine pit emptied if he wanted to? Our r.i.c.e. colleagues returned to Sitapur in December 2014 to find out.

One of the first things that they learnt was that latrine pits are so rarely emptied manually in villages that it is difficult to estimate the price of this service. The few families they found who had ever had a honeycomb-style pit emptied reported paying a very high price compared to what they pay for other services in villages.

A young Brahmin named Abhishek Sharma explained to our colleagues that his relatives had recently needed to get their pit emptied:

There is no one who will empty out a pit here. Near us, in 10, 20, 50 kilometres, there is no one who will empty out a pit. This is a problem. Our uncle's latrine pit got filled up. It was a soak [honeycomb-style] pit. We had to bring someone from Lucknow to get it emptied out. They took five-and-a-half thousand rupees for a two-hour job. That's why this is a big problem.

To put this price into perspective, an unskilled day labourer who works in Sitapur town could expect to earn about 200 rupees per day. He would earn even less if he were working in a village. An economist who is unaware of India's history of untouchability would be shocked by the high cost of getting a latrine pit emptied. How could someone charge 5,500 rupees for two hours of manual labour when the wage for day labour in the same market is so much less? For this much money, one could buy two complete latrines in Bangladesh! The economist, drawing upon the familiar model of supply and demand, would expect more workers to enter the market for latrine pit emptying and compete against one another for work until the price of the job came down.

The key reason why people who empty latrine pits can charge much more than the prevailing wage for day labour is that very, very few people are willing to do this work, even for high wages. The model of supply and demand itself is not wrong, but something unique is holding back supply in this case. While visiting an NGO that works on sanitation in Bihar, Diane and Nikhil met a field manager whose job was to convince people to adopt affordable latrines. Having talked to many villagers himself, the field manager understood that people did not want government latrines because they did not want to deal with having to empty latrine pits. He wondered if more people would adopt latrines if he were also able to offer a pit-emptying service. But he struggled to find people to provide those services. He explained, 'For [people who empty latrine pits] it is like this: If you earn well, but you can't go to a restaurant, and you can't go to a temple, what is the use?'

Earlier, we mentioned that one important limit on the pace of social progress in rural India is that higher castes are unwilling to perform traditionally untouchable work, even as more and more Dalits reject these forms of employment. But you might still be wondering whether, faced with such high prices, at least some higher-caste latrine owners would learn to swallow their distaste and empty the latrine pit themselves? After all, as Abhishek Sharma explained, it is a job that takes only a couple of hours.

We did meet a handful of people who had emptied or claimed to be willing to empty their own latrine pits. Most were Muslim. More often than not, they whispered to us that they had emptied the pit under the cover of darkness rather than pay the exorbitant price that a scavenger would charge.

But the vast majority of people we talked with said that they could not even conceive of emptying a latrine pit themselves. Priya, a woman living in peri-urban Sitapur who belonged to a lower, but not a Dalit, caste, explained why:

> We cannot empty [the latrine pit] ourselves. We call a Bhangi even if something gets clogged in the latrine ... How can we empty it ourselves? It is disgusting, so a Bhangi must come to clean it ... We are Hindus, so how can we clean it? [If we do], how will we worship afterwards? If money were an issue we would take a loan for it; we would have to find some way to get it emptied. This work can only be done by people who inherit this occupation. They are Bhangis, they have been created [by God] for this work.

Dalits from other than manual scavenging castes also refuse to empty their own latrine pits. A sixty-year-old Pasi (a traditionally pig-rearing Dalit caste) man who works as a nightwatchman explained:

> We can't empty it on our own. It's their occupation, they are the ones who do it. We are not that. They are the Mehtars, so they clean, but we are Pasi, so we can't clean … If we clean, we will [be ostracized] – nobody will smoke hookah with us – I mean that nobody will eat or drink with us if we clean [faeces] … People won't eat with us, and they won't drink water from our cups.

Sometimes, when we were interviewing people about latrines and pit emptying, we would explain how honeycomb-style latrine pits work. We did this because most people wrongly believe that if they are used daily, government latrine pits fill up very quickly, in a matter of two or three months. However, a 1.5-cubic-metre latrine pit that is used daily will actually fill up in a matter of years, not months. This is because the water used for flushing and the water content of the faeces seeps into the ground.

Incorrect beliefs about how long it takes a pit to fill up lead people to considerably overestimate the cost of owning a latrine. They think that they would have to pay several hundreds or thousands of rupees every few months to have the pit emptied. It is no wonder, then, that the SQUAT survey documented that people think that a latrine pit should be reserved for daughters-in-law, for old people, or for 'emergencies'. Pits are a depletable resource: The thinking goes that the more often they are used, the more money will have to be spent on emptying them. We suspect that correcting the false belief that pits fill up in a matter of months could be a good first step for a programme of behaviour change informed by the complaints rural Indians have about government latrines.

Another way that campaigns for change in sanitation behaviour–change campaigns might attempt to approach open defecation is by teaching people that decomposed faeces in twin-pit systems are less biologically dangerous than fresh sludge. After all, there is little chance that villagers will learn this from their neighbours. So few twin-pit latrines are in use that most people do not know that faeces decompose and become safer to handle. We hope that information could encourage people to view pit emptying differently.

However, we are not particularly optimistic that educating people about twin-pit technology would be enough to create behaviour change. After all, in Chapter 3, R.S. Khare and Damaris Lüthi explained that in places as distinct as Uttar Pradesh and Tamil Nadu, people are often far more concerned with ritual purity than with physical germs.

When Nikhil explained the use of twin pits to Abhishek Sharma, he did not challenge the ideas that the faeces would decompose, and that, biologically speaking, they would be less infectious. Nevertheless, he was firm that this new information did not change his thinking about pit emptying or his family members' thinking. He said, 'We will not be able to do it. I mean, this depends on your thinking and your "himmat". People *can* do it, but *we* can't do it.'

Several other people also referred to himmat when talking about pit emptying. We found this word choice revealing. Himmat typically translates to 'courage', but when our respondents used it to talk about pit emptying, they linked it to a person's 'thinking' or 'orientation' towards caste and untouchability. People with himmat were those who were willing to challenge social norms and face the stigma and ostracization that might accompany such an act.

In Bihar's Sheohar district, Diane and Nikhil finally met an older man who had the himmat that others were talking about. His name was Ashok Singh.

We arrived in his village early one morning in March 2015. We started by asking people whether they knew any families who owned a pit latrine. A young man who was walking with his bicycle through the village said that his father, Ashok, had a pit latrine and agreed to take us to his house to talk with him. When we got to the house, we had to wait a few minutes – Ashok was using his latrine.

Ashok told us that five years ago, he had received some money from the government to build the latrine. He added some of his own money and built two latrines, with separate pits. He had instructed the mason to dig the pits 1.5 metres deep instead of 0.9 metres deep, which was the depth he believed the government had been promoting at the time. He also had the mason construct a short wall for privacy. It was about four feet high, with no roof. Of the two latrines, only one was functional when we visited; the other had fallen into disrepair.

Ashok had recently emptied his latrine pit himself. At first, he thought about hiring a man from another village who belonged to a manual scavenging caste to empty it. But he thought that the man would want too much money for the job – 700 to 1,000 rupees – so Ashok decided to empty the pit himself. Ashok said that before emptying the pit, he had flushed five kilograms of lime into the pit, along with some kerosene, and left the pit alone for ten days. Then, he opened the cover, removed the sludge with a shovel and a cart and dumped it in the fields.

Nikhil and Diane were astonished. In many months of talking to people about latrine pits, this was the first and only time that a higher-caste person reported simply and matter-of-factly that he had emptied a latrine pit. Immediately, they wanted to know: Did Ashok not think that he would become polluted through contact with the faeces? Did he not think that others in the village would judge him for emptying the pit?

Ashok told Diane and Nikhil, 'Look, you are educated people ... If you had a piece of gold that fell into a pile of shit, would you not pick it up, wash it off and keep it? I don't think you would just leave it there.'

He also talked about how times are changing: Dalits are going to school and entering into politics. Even though not everyone he knows is willing to do it, more people are willing to sit down and eat with people from the Dalit castes. Ashok summarized, 'When untouchability is gone, the country will be free.'

The goal of this chapter has been to understand how people in rural India think about affordable latrines and what affordable latrines still have to do with untouchability. We have met many people who endorse or at least are unwilling to challenge casteist attitudes. They have also explained how these attitudes dissuade them from using affordable latrines. As common as these views are, in every population there are outliers and unusual people. We feel lucky to have met Ashok Singh, who explicitly rejects casteism and untouchability, and who is also willing to empty his own latrine pit. The difference in thinking, and in himmat, between the casteist many and the egalitarian few suggest that the right data could permit a statistical test of this chapter's conclusion: that casteism and rejection of affordable latrines go hand in hand.

You might think that such quantitative data would be difficult to come by. Few large surveys in India ask people about their social attitudes; fewer still also ask about sanitation. But, as we mentioned above, Amit Thorat, an economist from Jawaharlal Nehru University, asked respondents to the 2012 India Human Development Survey whether someone in their household practised untouchability – meaning whether they enforce untouchability in their interactions with Dalits. There was no verification or follow-up, merely an invitation to admit to discrimination, in a conversation with a stranger with a clipboard. Many rural Indians admitted it.

Are the places where people are most concerned about caste purity and untouchability also the places where people are least likely to use affordable latrines? In Chapter 2 we were left with a statistical puzzle, when no data could explain the pattern of open defecation in rural India and around the world. Now we have an explanation and the quantitative data to confirm it.

Dean collaborated with Amit Thorat to see whether this relationship held in the quantitative data. They found that indeed those villages where a higher fraction of people said that someone in their family practises untouchability are the same villages where a higher fraction of households defecates in the open – and not just because they are poorer or less well educated. Although, as the familiar adage holds, correlation is not causation, Dean and Amit are able to show that the association between open defecation and the practice of untouchability is specific, meaning that it is not the case that all other aspects of poverty or development similarly correlate with the practice of untouchability. Dean and Amit also find that living in a village where a higher fraction of households practises untouchability does not mean that people know less about health or germs; if anything, the opposite is true, perhaps because higher-caste people also tend to be better educated.

The fraction of households in a village that practises untouchability can also account for the puzzling pattern across Indian states that we saw in Chapter 2. Relatively rich and well-governed states like Tamil Nadu and Gujarat have almost as much rural open defecation as human development laggards Uttar Pradesh and Bihar, while the poor and remote north-eastern states have very low open defecation. This fits the pattern: Fewer households report practising untouchability in the culturally dissimilar north-east than in Uttar Pradesh, Bihar, Tamil Nadu and Gujarat.

This study is an example of quantitative and qualitative research working together to bring new evidence to a difficult question. Without many long qualitative interviews, we might have never thought of investigating this correlation, nor would we have known whether to believe it if we did. The lessons of the data and of the explanations villagers gave us for their own behaviour reinforce one another.

Is there a conflict between ending open defecation and ending untouchability?

Once we understand why Dalits do not want to empty latrine pits, and why most higher-caste Hindus will also not do it, it is no surprise that rural Indians reject the kinds of affordable, normal pit latrines that have been used to reduce open defecation in the rest of the developing world. Although a public health professional would recognize such latrines as life-saving, villagers associate them with manual scavenging and all the stigma, exclusion and humiliation that manual scavenging represents.

This allows us to answer a question that we posed earlier in the chapter: Why do rural Indians want such expensive toilets, sitting atop large pits? We now understand that it is because these pits need to be emptied only very infrequently. Some people told us that their pits would last 8–10 years, others said they would last 15–20 years. Still other latrine owners told us that they did not expect to have to empty their pits in their own lifetimes. When we asked one man why he did not make his latrine's pit any larger, he explained that nobody lives forever.

Moreover, when large pits are emptied, it is often done by machine, rather than by hand. Although most people who empty these pits by machine are Dalits, this work is not as stigmatizing as disposing of faeces by hand.

We sometimes ask ourselves a fanciful question: What would happen if everyone in rural India who defecates in the open were to magically begin using the type of latrine they can already afford? How would the latrine pits be emptied? What would be the consequences for Dalits, once there is suddenly so much more emptying of latrine pits to do? Would the economic power of demand sweep away the social constraints on supply? Or would a resurgence of something similar to manual scavenging begin to roll back the very slow progress towards social equality that India has made? Although we cannot know, we suspect this magic success might come at the cost of delaying the annihilation of caste.

If so, there is an even harder question: Would it be worth it? Are the social costs of manual pit emptying, in the special case of rural India, ethically justified by the health and human development benefits of latrine use? This is not a question we can answer. Perhaps we do not have to; after all, we possess no magical powers to cause the widespread use of affordable latrines. What is more likely, we think, is that casteism will remain, that rural incomes will increase slowly and that people will continue to adopt latrine use only when they can afford the kinds of expensive latrine pits that can be emptied using a machine. As we will see in Chapter 7, the richest villagers may already have irrevocably defined expensive latrines as the only socially acceptable sanitation option.

We hope that this is not true, and that there is a better, faster alternative to eliminating open defecation. Under such an alternative, more people would come to think and act like Ashok Singh. They would reject untouchability and gain the himmat to empty their own latrine pits. This is not a new idea: Both Ambedkar and Gandhi advocated that higher-caste people do their own dirty work as a way of combating casteism.

Unfortunately, our many conversations with rural Indians suggest that this path is narrow, and the way unclear. Nor is it necessarily guaranteed by generational change. Ashok Singh's own son did not share his father's progressive beliefs. He felt that people who ate with Dalits had 'abandoned their moral values'.

Consequences

5 | Health: Surviving and growing in childhood

The last three chapters answered one vexing question: Why has open defecation remained so common in rural India? The answer is that many rural Indians see good reasons to continue defecating in the open rather than use affordable latrines – reasons related to beliefs, values and norms about purity, pollution and untouchability. But resolving this question leads to another question: Why, then, should development policy bother to try to change rural sanitation at all? If people are happy with what they are doing, what is the policy challenge? A large majority of people in rural India think that open defecation is not a public policy issue at all. Are they right?

These questions come into even sharper focus when we remember just how bad the consequences can be when development policy strays from what poor people want. When experts who know little about the lives of the poor try to intervene in villages, it often ends up empowering local elites who have different interests than the poor. So, would it not be a better, more democratic idea to devote scarce development funds and attention to the problems that poor people see as important?

This question should give pause to organizations committed to pursuing poor people's own priorities. But before anyone answers yes, we should be sure that we are not overlooking any important costs of open defecation. This investigation is the task of these three chapters.

The three chapters in this part are about the consequences of open defecation – in this chapter for health, in the next for economic outcomes and, finally, for the elderly and the disabled. This chapter and the next will put you through the heaviest statistical exercise of the book. We cannot apologize because the consequences of open defecation are fundamentally about the numbers. Each child who dies or is stunted by early-life disease is a tragedy. At the beginning of the book we met one of them, and we will meet more. They are *many*: Open defecation in rural India is a human development disaster that does important, lasting harm to a great many people.

In this chapter, we use Indian data to show that something that has long been known to be true elsewhere is unsurprisingly also true in India – that exposure to poor sanitation is very bad for health. In the face of this stark and universal medical fact, India is special for two reasons. First, India has much more open defecation than any other country that is as rich. Second, the high population density in India – the fact that people live so close to one another and to one another's germs – would make any amount of open defecation all the more threatening.

Only since the nineteenth century have scientists understood that micro-organisms in faeces spread disease. Increasing worldwide application of the germ theory of disease is an important part of why human lives today are so much longer and better than only a few generations ago. The science of germs is relatively recent in human history: John Snow's pioneering demonstration of the unsanitary roots of cholera in London was published in the 1850s. Snow's main work was published only fifteen years before Mohandas Gandhi was born; Ambedkar, Gandhi, Jinnah and Nehru were all born before the first septic tank was patented in 1895.

This science quickly translated into rapid improvements in health and longevity. As the demographer Samuel Preston demonstrated, although richer populations tend to have longer lives than poorer populations, even poor populations today generally enjoy much longer lives than the rich societies of just a few generations ago. Economic growth cannot explain this improvement; rather, it is the dividend of basic knowledge and advances such as sanitation and applications of public health. This recent escape from disease and infant death is among the greatest stories humans have experienced. Still, the basic tenets of the germ theory unfortunately have yet to change much in many rural Indian villages.

Good toilets make good neighbours

Sixty years ago, Subedarganj served as a small market for British colonial infantrymen. Today, Uttar Pradesh state police are trained in the surrounding British-era buildings. Subedarganj itself is home to Muslims and lower-caste families who have moved in from the nearby villages. If you arrive in the evening, you will hear the slow and melodic azan over a crackly loudspeaker, calling Muslims to prayer. Men stroll and sit in a narrow street lined with vegetable stands, medicine shops, barbershops and liquor stores. At the first intersection, marked by a hand pump, a brick path leads to a row of houses at the edge of the settlement. One of these is the single-room home of our friend Baby.

For four years, Baby was Diane's guide and research assistant in Sitapur, a district north of Lucknow in the state of Uttar

Pradesh. Like most women in Uttar Pradesh, Baby is not much taller than Diane's shoulder. Unlike most women we know, she lives on her own without a husband, although her niece often stays with her. Marriage is all but compulsory in Uttar Pradesh. Still, somehow Baby has found the courage to provide for herself.

As worrisome as her lack of economic security may be, Baby is also preoccupied with establishing and maintaining a social identity, both within her family and among the neighbours. The basic lesson of rural Uttar Pradesh has not escaped her: You protect your role in the rigid social order by enforcing its rules. Despite all of the ways in which Uttar Pradesh's rigid social structure works against her, she talks about the differences she sees among social, caste and religious groups with a frank certainty that would make rich-country progressives gasp.

Baby lives in a single brick room that is mostly filled by a bed and a large metal box used to keep the thick winter quilts away from the bugs and mice. When she moved in, there was already a rudimentary latrine behind the house. To use it, Baby sits outside on a platform above a pan, which drains through a piece of pipe into a simple pit just outside her tiny patch of land. She added rocks around the seat to make the area less muddy during the rainy season. Because there is a brick boundary wall around the land at the back of the house, someone who is using the latrine cannot be seen by the neighbours. With only women in the house, latrine walls and a roof are not necessary. When Baby has guests, she sometimes props up a piece of sheet metal for privacy.

Early in our time in Uttar Pradesh, we were confused: So many villagers happily live without latrines. So why did Baby maintain this investment, when she had so little money to spare? Not for the first or last time, Baby explained something important: She uses a latrine because she is a Muslim. Everybody knows, she said, that the Hindus own either an impressively fancy latrine or no latrine at all. Muslims, Baby emphasized, are more interested in using a latrine even if they can only afford a simple one.

In showing us her latrine, Baby was not merely reminding us of how thoroughly the lives of people in rural Uttar Pradesh are governed by the social groups they belong to; she was also helping us begin to realize how sanitation turns upside down what we thought we knew about health in rural India. Muslims are poorer, on average, than Hindus are in India. Baby showed us a poorer group of people that is more likely to use latrines than their richer neighbours.

Baby's latrine was the small piece that helped us begin putting together the pieces of a puzzle in the economics of health: the Muslim mortality paradox. This puzzle was named by economists Sonia Bhalotra, Christine Valente and Arthur van Soest. Using the Indian government's National Family Health Survey data, they documented that Muslim babies in India are more likely than Hindu babies in India to survive childhood. Of every 1,000 babies reported in the survey rounds that they studied, seventy-four died before their fifth birthday. This terrible average conceals a large inequality: Fouteen more Hindu babies died before their fifth birthday than Muslim babies.

This is a large difference in a baby's chances of survival. What makes this fact not merely tragic but also paradoxical is that Muslims are, in many other ways, a disadvantaged minority in India. Ordinarily, richer babies are more likely to survive and poorer babies are more likely to die. Yet, Muslim children come from poorer families than Hindu children, on average, and have less well educated mothers and families. Bhalotra and her colleagues carefully documented that the standard measures that economists use for socio-economic status, such as parents' education and household asset ownership, can collectively explain none of the Muslim mortality advantage.

To look for solutions for this puzzle, Dean teamed up with Mike Geruso, an economics professor. Mike, Dean and a long line of medical doctors and researchers knew that open defecation spreads disease that can kill babies: Diarrhoea is only the most obvious cause. They also now knew that Muslims in India are less likely to defecate in the open than Hindus.

Could open defecation – not only of a child's own parents and siblings, but also of his whole neighbourhood – explain the Muslim mortality paradox? As the name implies, open defecation takes place in the open – usually away from one's own home. Perhaps what matters for infant survival is not whether or not the people in a child's own household defecate in the open, but the fraction of his neighbours that defecates in the open. The fraction of a village or neighbourhood that defecates in the open may offer a far better measure of a child's exposure to disease in the environment than simply whether his own parents own a toilet.

If so, the role of religion in Indian society would become important. Muslims tend to live near other Muslims and Hindus tend to live near other Hindus. In combination with the fact that Muslims are less likely to defecate in the open, this adds up to a large difference in babies' disease environments. According to the same national data used by Bhalotra, Valente and van Soest, 66 per cent of the average Hindu baby's neighbours defecate in the open, compared with only 45 per cent of the average Muslim baby's neighbours. This striking 21 percentage point difference is larger than the difference between sub-Saharan Africa, where 23 per cent of people defecate in the open, and Latin America, where less than 3 per cent of people defecate in the open.

When we first started working with the Muslim mortality paradox, we did not originally understand the causes of this large difference in sanitation behaviour within India. Having read the last three chapters, you now know more than we did at the time about why open defecation is so prevalent in India. To study the consequences for child health, though, it is enough for now that this large statistical difference exists.

Open defecation and infant mortality

Neighbours matter. What looked like a Muslim survival advantage turns out to be a Muslim *neighbour* survival advantage. Hindu babies who live in villages where they are surrounded by many Muslims are just as likely to survive as Muslim babies with the same fraction of Muslim neighbours. This fact is important for two reasons. First, it rules out religion itself (along with other private behaviours) as an explanation for the paradox: Muslims may eat different foods than Hindus, for example, but this could not explain an effect on the survival of their neighbours' children. Second, it is evidence that the apparent health benefits of latrine use over open defecation do not actually, misleadingly, reflect some other form of neighbourhood-level advantage, such as overall infrastructure or government services. Villages and neighbourhoods with more Muslims are similar or disadvantaged on essentially every other dimension that is important for infant health. So, if children are less likely to die in places with more Muslims, regardless of their own religion, this is strong evidence that open defecation can explain the difference in child survival.

Indeed, it can. Mike and Dean compared Hindu babies and Muslim babies who matched on the fraction of their neighbours who defecated in the open. Once children were matched so that there was no Hindu–Muslim difference in exposure to open defecation, they found that there was no Hindu–Muslim difference in mortality either: Babies of either religion were similarly likely to die at the same level of neighbourhood sanitation. So, neighbourhood sanitation can account for the Muslim mortality paradox. It is no paradox at all that babies exposed to fewer faecal germs are more likely to survive.

It is difficult to estimate precisely how many children die due to open defecation in India each year. One difficulty lies in the fact that the health effects of open defecation are differently large in different places, even within India – as we will see later in this chapter, for example, the same amount of open defecation is more deadly where population density is higher. A conservative estimate, based on the research by Mike and Dean and on other data sources, is that perhaps over 200,000, and almost certainly over 100,000, children under five die each year who would otherwise survive if there were no open defecation in India. If so, the number of children under five who die in India each year due to open defecation is greater than the number of Americans of all ages who die from accidents, unintentional injuries and diabetes combined; is greater than the number who die from stroke and Alzheimer's disease combined; and is perhaps as much as one half of the number who die each year, mostly at older ages, of cancer. If this is true, and if the effects of open defecation remain similar in the coming decades, over five million Indian children may die before open defecation is eliminated, if the decline continues at the same slow rate.

Although these numbers are necessarily imprecise, one fact is certain: Some of these children who are killed by open defecation live in families where everybody uses a toilet or latrine to safely dispose of their faeces. Both Hindu babies and Muslim babies are more likely to survive childhood when fewer of their neighbours defecate in the open, whether their family uses a latrine or not. Open defecation is not merely a threat to the health of the families who do it; open defecation is everybody's business.

The long and short of it: The average height of children

If you have a big enough data set, you will perhaps find that richer people are taller than poorer people – not each individual person, but on average. This pattern is too subtle, too imperfect to be seen among the handful of people we meet each day. But even though you cannot see it, the correlation of height with economic advantage is well-known among statistical researchers. Among the many reasons for this are that richer families, typically with better-educated parents, are able to raise their children in healthier environments. We care about how tall or short a population is because it is a marker for how healthy that population was when they were children, and therefore, of how well their brains and bodies were able to develop.

Compared to people in other poor countries, people in India are very short. Some of the world's poorest people live in sub-Saharan Africa, where extreme poverty is twice as common as in India. Yet, people in India are shorter, on average, than people in almost every other large population – even shorter than people in sub-Saharan Africa.

Researchers have named this puzzle the Asian Enigma. This is actually a misleading name – it is really an Indian Enigma.

The heights of other Asians are not similarly puzzling. For example, when we speak in India about this height research, we are often asked about height in Japan as though it were a counter-example – Japanese people appear to have a reputation in Indian circles for being short. Yet, 2009 OECD data shows that the average Japanese male is 172 centimetres tall, which is a little taller than the average man in Portugal or South Korea, a little shorter than men in Spain and much taller than the average man in India. According to the 2005 National Family Health Survey, the average man in India was only 164 centimetres tall. Similarly, children in China are much taller than children in India; the gap between the average Indian child and the average height of the WHO's reference table for healthy populations is twice as large as the gap for the average child living in China, where open defecation is nearly eliminated.

In the rest of this chapter, we will attempt to solve the Asian Enigma, meaning the Indian Enigma. Because it would not qualify as an enigma if it were not complex, the path will be winding. Along the way we will address a common incorrect answer, we will learn what we can from other comparisons of population heights, and we will review the science behind the effect of disease on child height.

To make comparisons simple, we will translate height differences into their implications for an average five-year-old girl. Using this yardstick, the Asian Enigma is that the average five-year-old girl in India is about two-thirds of a centimetre shorter than in sub-Saharan Africa. 'Two-thirds of a centimetre' may sound small, but it amounts to a five-year-old having missed thirty-eight days' worth of growth. Added up over hundreds of millions of children, this gap represents an enormous waste of human potential and well-being.

Differences in population height: Environment, not genetics

How could a richer country consistently produce shorter children? One common incorrect guess is genetics. Could it be that Indians inherit a shorter genetic potential height from their parents than other groups of people? Invoking genetic fate may be a convenient dodge for Indian politicians and bureaucrats – after all, such biological destiny would excuse them from their responsibility to improve the health of mothers and children. But there is no evidence that the world's populations could not all grow to the same average height if they and their mothers were similarly healthy.

History is full of examples of populations that were thought to be genetically short, but whose children grew taller when early-life conditions improved. There was a time when people thought that the two ethnic groups within Guatemala – the taller Ladinos, of Spanish descent, and the much shorter Mayans, of indigenous descent – were genetically predisposed to different heights. Anthropologist Barry Bogin documented that the difference between average Ladino and Mayan adults was a striking 10 centimetres. But when civil war broke out and thousands of Mayans began to take refuge in the United States, Bogin found that their children grew to be even taller than most Ladinos. Within one generation of improved early-life health, the Mayans' growth demonstrated that their short stature in Guatemala was due to severe environmental deprivation and not due to a genetic predisposition to shortness.

Sometimes, it does not even take a generation's worth of time for heights to improve. Lemm Proos, of Uppsala University, tracked Indian children adopted into Sweden. These migrant babies brought their Indian genetics into a Scandinavian environment. The adopted children grew almost as tall as average Swedish children. Moreover, children who were adopted earlier in infancy, and therefore exposed to a healthier environment earlier, grew taller than children adopted later in life.

Even among relatively well-off populations, population heights change over time. Europeans today are much taller than Europeans only a century or two ago – a fact palpable in the low ceilings and door frames of old buildings. Economist Timothy Hatton assembled historical data to show that the average European male was 11 centimetres taller in 1980 than in the mid-nineteenth century. In a conclusion that previews what we shall see about the Asian Enigma, Hatton finds 'that the most important proximate source of increasing height was the improving disease environment as reflected by the fall in infant mortality'. Income, education, family size and healthcare were all less important than the disease environment. Another recent change in average height has occurred rapidly in South Korea, where incomes and education levels have grown rapidly since the 1960s. Unfortunately, in North Korea, where most of the population is poor, young adults are not much taller than their parents and grandparents.

Although the evidence stands firmly against the proposition that child stunting in India is genetically heritable at the population level, or that any other population-level difference in average height is, it is worth pausing to consider the strangeness of this claim. Any large heritable difference in population-level average height could only be sustained through natural selection, the evolutionary process that gradually selects for reproductive fitness. The first humans in India migrated out of Africa only perhaps 75,000 years ago, and there has certainly been much migration and intermarriage since then. To our knowledge, nobody has offered a theoretical reason to believe that being shorter has somehow helped diminutive Indians to relatively successfully reproduce since these recent common ancestors *by so much* as to produce a large height difference in these few thousand generations. Such a theory would also have to explain why its mechanisms did not similarly also advantage short people in other places, because the goal would be to explain why only Indians are genetically shorter. At the risk of disappointing any politicians who would rather not tackle a difficult policy challenge, we must abandon genetics in our search for the answer to the enigma.

Is there a Bengali enigma too?

The short stature of Indian children is a solvable problem, not a genetic fact. The ability of average population height to change is particularly visible in a comparison between children in West Bengal and children in neighbouring Bangladesh. Dean studied these children along with two collaborators, Arabinda Ghosh and Aashish Gupta. These two regions offer a special test case. There is no doubt that both groups of children are from a similar Bengali population. They were split into two separate countries only in 1947, an evolutionary instant ago, and there is still much migration between them today.

On average, Bangladeshi people are poorer than Indians. GDP per capita in Bangladesh is less than two-thirds of what it is in India. People in West Bengal are more likely to have a radio than people in Bangladesh, are more than twice as likely to have a bicycle or a motorcycle and are more than four times as likely to have a phone. So, it is no surprise that children in West Bengal are taller than children in Bangladesh. The average five-year-old girl in West Bengal is about a quarter of a centimetre taller than the average five-year-old girl in Bangladesh.

Taking wealth into consideration turns this picture upside down. Comparing similarly rich or poor children in Bangladesh and West Bengal, the average child in Bangladesh is *taller* than the average child in West Bengal. Returning to our average five-year-old girl, she is half a centimetre taller in Bangladesh than an equally rich or poor girl in West Bengal.

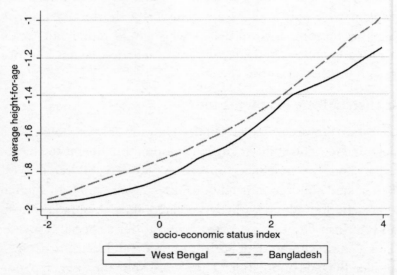

Figure 6. Children in Bangladesh are taller than children in West Bengal, at the same level of wealth or poverty

Figure 6 documents this difference, using data from Demographic and Health Surveys. The horizontal axis of the graph is a measure of the wealth of the child's household, based on the questions the survey asked about what the family owns. It is scaled to the average child, so a socio-economic status of zero means an average wealth, in this graph. The vertical axis is a measure of how tall children are, relative to international norms for healthy children. Researchers have shown that relatively privileged children in south Delhi grow according to these healthy norms, on average, but most children in India do not. That is why the height numbers are negative. The average child is unhealthily short both in West Bengal and in Bangladesh.

The curves present the average height of children at each level of household wealth. Overall, the average child in West Bengal is taller than the average child in Bangladesh, but here, the solid line for West Bengal is always below the dashed line for Bangladesh. That is because this graph accounts for household poverty: Equivalently rich or poor children in Bangladesh grow taller.

This poses another, smaller enigma. Why are children in West Bengal shorter than equivalently poor Bangladeshis? Despite the economic disadvantage of Bangladesh, there are many ways in which Bangladeshis enjoy better lives than Indians, especially women. Women in Bangladesh are more likely than women in India to be able to read and to have jobs. So, one part of the explanation is that better educated and freer Bangladeshi mothers can raise healthier children.

An additional difference between Bangladeshi villages and Indian villages is open defecation. In 2005, when child height was last measured throughout India, 57.1 per cent of Indians defecated in the open, compared to only 12.1 per cent of Bangladeshis, according to UNICEF and the WHO. Since then, open defecation in Bangladesh has almost been eliminated; less than 3 per cent of people defecated in the open in 2012. As open defecation has declined in Bangladesh over time, successive cohorts of children have grown taller.

This suggests that open defecation is a possible explanation for the Bangladeshi height advantage. When Arabinda, Aashish and Dean looked at the data, they found that Bangladeshi children are no taller than equally poor children in West Bengal who are exposed to similar levels of open defecation. Thus, open defecation can statistically account for this gap. Of course, open defecation is not the only difference between West Bengal and Bangladesh that matters. But it is an important one.

Living close and growing apart in rural Uttar Pradesh

When people ask us how we chose our home in rural Uttar Pradesh, we explain that we wanted to learn about a place with short children and high infant mortality. So, when we arrived in 2011, Diane put together a plan to study child development by visiting newborns in three nearby villages. As a demographer, she is most likely to tell you about the statistical properties of babies in the thousands. But she double-checks her computations against what these children and their mothers have taught her over the years.

With Baby's help, Diane chose villages that were cycling distance from our house, so that the two of them could visit again and again. The villages have diverse populations of both Hindus and Muslims, higher-caste children and lower-caste children, richer children and poorer children. In February of 2012, Baby and Diane knocked on every door in all three villages to ask whether the family had a baby less than one month old. Because height can also be influenced by experiences that occur when a child is in the womb, they also asked to meet women who were in the late stages of pregnancy. In the end, twenty pregnant women and new mothers agreed to let Diane and Baby be a small part of their lives.

Two of the babies are Anil and Arun. Watching Anil and Arun grow revealed much about the important interactions between nutrition and infection. At first glance, these boys seem to have a lot in common. Their villages are close to one another. They both live in large extended families that own and farm land. They are both the first child born to their mothers. They both belong to the Yadav caste, a powerful Hindu caste in this part of central Uttar Pradesh. Yet, their health has diverged radically.

Anil's mother stopped breastfeeding him when he was less than two months old because she got mastitis, an infection in her breast that is common among breastfeeding mothers. Rather than continuing to breastfeed while taking antibiotics to clear the infection, as is recommended, she started giving Anil buffalo milk, mixed with water, and her body stopped making breast milk. The switch from breast milk to watery buffalo milk at such a young age had doubly negative consequences for Anil's growth. First, it is not the right kind of nutrition for a small baby. Neither buffalo milk nor cow milk has the easy-to-digest proteins found in breast milk, which babies need for growth; nor do they have human antibodies, which babies need to fight disease.

Second, bottle-feeding exposed Anil to germs. These germs lived in the milk, which was not always properly boiled, and especially on the bottle, which was rarely sterilized with boiling water. When Anil got tired of drinking milk, he often dropped the bottle in the dirt. Flies landed on the nipple to steal a sip of milk. His mother simply picked it up, wiped the dirt off on her clothes and handed it back to him.

Exposure to so many germs without enough nutrition to fight them made Anil so sick that he nearly died several times before he was three years old. He suffered from diarrhoea and bloody stools. He underwent several months of treatment for tuberculosis. By the time he was two-and-a-half years old, Anil was only 80 centimetres tall, which is the height of a healthy sixteen-month-old: His physical growth was more than a full year behind his age.

Arun, on the other hand, was born into the extended family of his village's pradhan, the elected village chairman. His great-uncle was pradhan for many years. At the time Diane met him, political affirmative action legally required that the position of pradhan be reserved for a member of the lowest-ranking castes, but one gets the impression that Arun's great-uncle still wields political power in the village even when he is technically not the pradhan.

There was plenty to eat in Arun's house, and his mother ate well during pregnancy. After Arun was born, she spent most of her time at her parents' home in her home village. This meant she did not have to do hard work and could focus on breastfeeding him as often as he wanted. The result of these good early-life experiences was that Arun grew much larger than Anil did. At two years and nine months, Arun was 89 centimetres tall. Arun is not tall by international standards – in fact, he is only at the tenth percentile of heights among healthy children – but, unlike Anil, his height at least registers on the growth charts.

When Mike and Dean were studying the consequences of open defecation for infant mortality among Hindus and Muslims, they saw reflected in statistics the interaction between disease and breastfeeding that Arun and Anil experienced. Breastfeeding promotes survival for all children, both Hindu and Muslim. But the difference in infant mortality between babies who are exclusively breastfed and babies who are not is smaller, on average, for Muslims than for Hindus. In other words, the statistics initially appear to suggest that breastfeeding is somehow less protective against mortality for Muslims than breastfeeding is for Hindus.

But this is merely a telling statistical illusion. This difference emerges only because the average Hindu baby faces more disease that she needs protection from. Breastfeeding is a barrier against the germs spread by open defecation, and more of the average Hindu baby's neighbours defecate in the open. So, in practice, breastfeeding turns out to matter more for the average Hindu baby, because the average Hindu baby is surrounded by more faecal germs.

A closer look at the data confirms that breastfeeding is equally good for Hindu and Muslim babies if they are equally exposed to open defecation. This interaction between breastfeeding and open defecation is a reason to be confident that the Muslim mortality paradox is about sanitation: There is no other good way to explain what would otherwise be a new Muslim breastfeeding puzzle.

The fact that Anil got buffalo milk and Arun got breast milk probably made a big contribution to how well they were able to fight the diseases that they encountered. Almost every rural person that either of these boys has ever met defecates in the open. So, faecal germs were an important threat to these boys, and breastfeeding would have offered relevant protection.

But there is something else that was probably important too. The time that Arun and his mother spent in her parents' home after he was born was perhaps protective against disease. Even though Arun will probably one day be the head of a powerful village family, his earliest and most formative years were spent living with his maternal grandparents, in an urban neighbourhood outside the district capital. In this part of Uttar Pradesh, such neighbourhoods typically have less open defecation than a village, where almost everyone defecates in the open. By spending much of his growing years in a place with better sanitation, among other advantages, Arun was exposed to less disease.

How faecal germs do their dirty work

Open defecation deposits faeces on the ground. In India, this means that germs are close to where other people live and work. Flies land on these germs; adults step on them; and children play in dirt contaminated with them. Like Anil's bottle, or the finger a mother offers for a crying baby to suck, there are countless ways for these ubiquitous faecal germs to make their way to growing children.

The most obvious consequence is diarrhoea. Diarrhoea is a short-term disease spread by faecal germs. When a person has diarrhoea, her body is trying to flush out harmful viruses or bacteria. A side effect is that the body also purges itself of whatever food the person has eaten recently. This means that the person cannot absorb the nutrition in that food and use it to grow.

Environmental enteric dysfunction may be another disease that keeps children exposed to open defecation from growing as tall as they could. Environmental enteropathy is not yet perfectly understood, but scientists are making progress towards understanding how important this chronic condition may be. Repeated exposure to faecal germs may lead to a threatening combination: a flattening of the folds of the intestine, which are necessary for the absorption of nutrients in food, combined with an increased permeability of the intestines to disease. A child with enteropathy may not look sick on the outside, but she would nevertheless grow up to be shorter than her genetic potential height, if her body is less able to convert the food she eats into energy for growth.

Open defecation also spreads parasites. Parasites live and lay their eggs in human intestines. When people with parasitic infections defecate in the open, the parasites' eggs are exposed on the ground for other people to encounter.

These parasites stifle child growth in a number of ways. First, they quite literally steal a child's food: They use the food she eats to grow and reproduce themselves. Parasites growing in a child's intestines also cause loss of appetite and, sometimes, scarring and bleeding in the intestines that make it difficult to digest food. Ascariasis, commonly known as roundworm, is the most common type of intestinal worm in India. Its larvae burrow through the host's intestine and mature in the host's lungs. Hookworm attaches itself to the wall of the host's intestine and feeds on their blood.

Unfortunately, there is no nationally representative survey data on intestinal parasitic infections in India, but studies in different locations suggest that infection rates are high, especially in rural areas. One study from twenty rural schools in Bihar found that almost 70 per cent of children had at least one kind of parasite infection.

───⌇───

These types of diseases – diarrhoea, enteropathy and parasitic infections – could transform exposure to widespread open defecation into child stunting. Disease may also matter indirectly, by consuming the body's energy while fighting an infection or by weakening the immune system so that the child is more vulnerable to respiratory infections.

These diseases probably also have implications for nutritional outcomes other than height. One important example is anaemia, a condition in which people have too little of the protein haemoglobin in their blood. It is a disease with worrisome consequences – anaemic children feel tired and irritable and do not grow up to achieve as much on learning tests as children who are not anaemic. Anaemic adults are not able to work as hard as healthy adults, and women with anaemia are at an increased risk of dying during childbirth.

Like stunting, anaemia is a far more common in India than in most other places in the developing world. The latest national data on anaemia found that about 70 per cent of young children were anaemic in 2005. The only other places with such high rates of anaemia are those parts of Africa with high rates of malaria, a disease caused by a parasite that feeds off haemoglobin. In India, however, malaria does not have the same extent of bad consequences.

For years, the response of the Indian public health community to anaemia has been to prescribe iron supplements because it is a nutrient that the body needs to produce haemoglobin. This strategy implicitly overlooks the nutritional consequences of disease. In much the same way that the diseases of open defecation make children short, they could also be contributing to high rates of anaemia. In addition to iron, the body needs folate and vitamins B6 and B12 to produce haemoglobin. If children are not able to absorb these nutrients because they have frequent diarrhoea, chronic enteropathy or parasite infections, their bodies will not be able to fully use the nutrients in their food or in special dietary supplements.

Although there is still much to learn about the relationship between open defecation and anaemia, evidence suggests that open defecation may be an important contributor to anomalously high rates of anaemia in South Asia. The same type of demographic survey data that we use to study child height and infant mortality can be used to investigate the relationship between open defecation and the haemoglobin levels of children in Nepal. Nepal is a good place to study this relationship because, unlike in India, many households in Nepal have been making the switch from open defecation to toilet or latrine use over the past decade. In 2006, about half of Nepali households defecated in the open, but by 2011 that fraction had declined to 35 per cent.

Some regions within Nepal had more improvement in open defecation than others, so it makes sense to ask whether those were the same regions that had the most relative improvements in children's haemoglobin levels. They are: On average, trends in haemoglobin levels were more favourable in regions where open defecation had fallen more quickly than in regions where open defecation had fallen more slowly. If open defecation is an important cause of anaemia in India, policymakers should expect limited success from programmes that concentrate on distributing supplement pills that diseased intestines will not absorb.

Deciphering the Asian (Indian) Enigma

We now have the knowledge of disease, nutrition and growth that we need to return to the Asian Enigma, the question of why children in India are shorter than children in sub-Saharan Africa. To review: Average heights of populations are shaped by the environment to which they are exposed and not by genes. There are many important parts of that environment. These include the nutrition and the health of mothers during pregnancy and early childhood (which, as in the case of Arun's mother, can reflect her social status and empowerment), and include whether and how the child is breastfed. One important part of the environment is disease, which can be shaped by sanitation. Diarrhoea, enteropathy and parasites are three important biological mechanisms by which open defecation could make Indian children shorter than they otherwise would be. Could differences in open defecation explain the Asian Enigma of shorter children in India than in sub-Saharan Africa?

We can begin to answer by recognizing that the difference between India and sub-Saharan Africa in open defecation is large. In 2005, the last year with reliable data, open defecation was approximately half as common in sub-Saharan Africa as it was in India. According to UNICEF–WHO estimates, at that time, 57 per cent of Indians defecated in the open. Open defecation was much less common even in poor African countries; for example, it was 15 per cent in Kenya, 11 per cent in the Democratic Republic of the Congo and only 4 per cent in Rwanda. African children may not have as much money as Indian children, but they are much freer from the disease spread by a neighbour's open defecation. The fact that the difference in average exposure to open defecation is so large between India and sub-Saharan Africa means that an effect of open defecation on child height would not have to be very large for poor sanitation to be quantitatively able to explain the height difference.

Open defecation is only one of many threats to the health and height of growing children. To know whether open defecation could explain the gap in child height between India and sub-Saharan Africa, we would have to know how big the effect of open defecation is. Is the effect of open defecation big enough to account for the two-thirds of a centimetre shortfall of the average Indian five-year-old girl?

When Dean first asked whether open defecation could explain the Asian Enigma, he started by comparing children exposed to similar threats in large demographic data sources that are representative of the whole of India and sub-Saharan Africa. Children in India are shorter, overall, but they are also exposed to much more open defecation.

What about children in India and sub-Saharan Africa who are exposed to the *same amount* of open defecation? In this case, there is no difference in child height and no Asian Enigma. In places where African children are exposed to the same density of neighbours who defecate in the open, they are every bit as short as Indian children. In other words, if open defecation density matches, average child height does too.

Converging evidence on open defecation and child height

Is the puzzle resolved? Does it settle the matter that Indian children and African children match on average height when they match on exposure to open defecation? This is an important evidence that open defecation can explain the enigma, but we should not stop there. After all, just as there are many differences between Bangladesh and West Bengal, there are even more differences between India and sub-Saharan Africa. So, it is important to make sure that what looks like an effect of open defecation is not actually an effect of something else.

Statistical researchers use a range of tools to separate real effects in which we should have confidence from merely apparent effects – coincidences, misleading correlations or other flukes of the data. Many researchers believe that the strongest conclusions emerge when multiple research strategies point in the same direction. Some approaches take the form that we have seen in the match between children in India and in sub-Saharan Africa – careful comparisons of large databases that are representative of entire populations. Other approaches focus on smaller samples of people in order to learn from special cases where cause and effect are unusually clearly linked.

Across a range of research strategies, open defecation has proven important for child height. One method compares countries – children from countries with more open defecation are shorter than children from countries with less open defecation. This is not just because countries with more open defecation are poorer – after all, there is more open defecation in India than in Bangladesh or sub-Saharan Africa.

Another approach looks across places within India – children from districts within India with more open defecation are also shorter than children from districts with less open defecation. And looking closer still, children from villages within India with more open defecation are shorter than children from villages with less open defecation.

Rather than studying the differences in open defecation that exist in the world, an alternative approach sets out to generate differences. When medical researchers test new drugs, they often conduct a randomized trial. Although toilets are not pills, the same principle could be applied to open defecation. Instead of randomly assigning some patients to receive a potent pill and other patients to a control group that receives a placebo, a research team could randomly assign some villages to 'receive' a reduction in open defecation and other villages to 'receive' a control treatment that leaves sanitation behaviour the way it was.

Of course, it is not that simple. In many cases, open defecation is something that people choose to do. If the researchers cannot persuade people in the study villages to stop defecating in the open, there will be little hope of learning about health effects by comparing the two groups of villages: In the end, their exposure to faecal germs will stay the same. The guiding principle of such an experiment is 'let's change open defecation and see what happens to health', but if you cannot change open defecation, you are out of luck. Similarly, if you decide to conduct a sanitation experiment in a place that has very little or no open defecation to begin with, you may learn important things, but there will be no opportunity to learn about the consequences of reducing open defecation because there will be no open defecation to reduce.

Despite these challenges, various research teams have mounted large-scale experiments on open defecation in villages. In particular, the World Bank organized a set of four experiments, each in a separate country and each attempting to generate changes in open defecation that researchers could learn from. Economist Paul Gertler collaborated with a team of researchers in a statistical study that combined data from four experiments, three of which included data to compute the effect of open defecation on child height. The combined study found that open defecation is important for child height. Gertler and his co-authors quantify the effect, averaging across these three studies, to be of precisely the magnitude necessary for open defecation to explain the Asian Enigma. Of course, even a perfect study can only narrow an estimate down to a range, not a single number – and the real effect of open defecation on child height is different in different places.

Another sanitation experiment was conducted by the World Bank and the health ministry of Maharashtra in 2004, in a far-sighted early effort to learn as much as possible about the health consequences of sanitation. About a decade later, Dean worked with economist Jeff Hammer to analyse the data that survived from the experiment. In the place the experiment was conducted, the data appears to show clear evidence of a large effect of open defecation on child height. Unfortunately, however, the experiment that happened was only conducted in one district out of the three districts that the original research team had planned. Statistically, this district appears to be the one where the programme was most likely to show an impressive effect; for example, more mothers are literate there.

No records explain quite how the experiment was steered only to this district or why the other districts were ignored. So, it is difficult to know what conclusions can be drawn from the results with confidence and what such conclusions would tell about places outside of that district in Maharashtra.

Many people, many germs

Why might open defecation have different consequences for health in different places? Knowing about the severe consequences for health of widespread open defecation, it would seem bad enough that most people in India defecate in the open. But the situation in India turns out to be even worse than these facts alone suggest. The same fraction of people defecating in the open is more harmful for child health in India than in the average developing country. This is because where population density is greater – meaning, where more people live together in smaller geographic areas – germs spread more easily.

To investigate how the density of open defecation matters to child health, we worked with a team of researchers – Payal Hathi, Sabrina Haque and Lovey Pant – to match data on sanitation and health from throughout the developing world with census counts of population density. We found that the same exposure to open defecation matters approximately twice as much in densely populated South Asia as it does in sub-Saharan Africa, on average.

This data also speaks to an old question among demographers: Is it better for a child's health to live in a city or in the countryside? The answer is that it depends, in part, on the density of open defecation. Children are more likely to survive and grow taller in clean and sanitary cities than in equally sanitary rural places, presumably because of easier access to healthcare and other resources. But children are more likely to die when exposed closely to neighbours' open defecation, which is all the more threatening in densely packed environments, including cities. Because this interaction between sanitation and population density makes epidemiological sense – germs are more threatening where they are more easily transmitted – these results give us one more reason to conclude that open defecation matters for health.

These results also underscore the threat to Indian children. Among large countries, India has one of the highest population densities in the world – 1.3 billion people live in a land area that is only one-third the size of the United States. India contains one in every six people alive in the world today, and the country's largest state, Uttar Pradesh, is home to one in every eight people worldwide who defecates in the open. The state contains a population as numerous as Brazil's in a land area smaller than Ecuador and slightly larger than the United Kingdom, or approximately as large as the US state of Michigan. The state's population is almost twice as dense as New Jersey's, the densest of any US state.

In densely populated India, widespread open defecation is especially disastrous. This coincidence appears to be a horrible accident of demography. It is humanity's bad luck that one-fifth of all births are in the country with most of the world's open defecation, which just so happens to be a country with very high population density.

There are still important open questions about the consequences of open defecation for health. For example, biological researchers are still asking how important the mechanisms of enteropathy will prove to be. In our own research, we have begun to wonder how widespread open defecation may shape the usefulness of deworming medicine. And, until somebody devises a programme that can quickly flip villages from open defecation to latrine use, it will remain difficult to learn about health effects of open defecation in rural India from a randomized, controlled experiment. Even then, the effects might be very different the next state over, if population density changes along the way.

Despite these open questions, what is clear is that the Asian Enigma is not so enigmatic any more. A variety of studies, taking a range of statistical approaches, reach compatible conclusions. Children in India are short but they are not puzzlingly short – they are as short as we would expect, knowing the amount of open defecation to which they are exposed. Similarly, the paradox of Muslim infant survival is no paradox, in light of the disadvantage that the average Hindu child faces from her neighbours' open defecation.

Of course, none of this should be interpreted to mean that open defecation is the only important constraint on early-life health in rural India. Unfortunately, this is far from the case. One other important problem is maternal nutrition. In India, babies tend to be born to young, low-status women who are far too likely to be underweight and who gain too little weight during pregnancy. Another problem is poor feeding practices – too few babies are given colostrum, a mother's especially nutritious first milk; too few are exclusively breastfed for six months; and too few transition appropriately to solid food. All of these problems interact. Poor breastfeeding makes the effects of open defecation worse, and a bad disease environment is one of the causes of underweight among adult women. The social and cultural forces that promote open defecation are related to those that constrain young mothers, especially in traditional households, and discourage proper early-life nutrition.

Open defecation kills children and stunts the growth of those who survive. It explains why some poorer children are more likely to survive than some richer children and it lets children in some of the poorest countries grow taller than children born in an India that has been experiencing rapid economic growth. These facts average over all Indians: Open defecation is a relatively egalitarian health hazard. Almost everyone lives near someone who defecates in the open. Money cannot buy a complete escape from an environment dense with germs. Open defecation poses a potential threat to the health of every Indian child.

6 | Economics: Children's human capital, adults' wages

Holi is a time to meet old friends. In the spring of 2015, just after the Hindu festival of the spring harvest, Diane and Baby patched up and reinflated the tyres on their bicycles. They made rounds to the three villages where they have been visiting babies since early 2012. The babies were becoming children: most of them had turned three years old.

All along, Diane had been measuring the growth of their bodies. Now it was time to measure the growth of their minds. In rich countries or in cities like Delhi, a psychologist might do this by showing cards with pictures of familiar shapes or colours. But Diane packed a bag of objects that would be familiar to children growing up in villages: a key, some rope, a spoon, a steel food container, a pen, a toothbrush, a photo, a potato, an onion, a bit of electrical wire and a piece of cotton. In the first village, Diane and Baby also had a ball and a coin, but these proved to be disruptive. Three-year-olds understandably find throwing a ball and buying snacks more engaging than demonstrating their vocabulary.

The group of three-year-olds whom Diane was visiting started as a cohort of twenty newborns and pregnant women. Of these, sixteen children had survived. Among the survivors, there was a wide range of variation in how well they performed on the test. Such variation is a bad outcome. Almost all healthy three-year-olds should be able to pay attention to a visitor and name these familiar objects. Unfortunately, Diane was not surprised by the diversity of cognitive development among the children. She and Baby had watched many of them repeatedly fall ill in the past three years.

The last chapter documented the consequences of open defecation for children's health: It was implicitly dedicated to the four babies who had died by the spring of 2015. This chapter is about the survivors. When young children are growing, their bodies, brains and minds are all developing together. If a child barely survives poor nutrition or disease in infancy, she misses out on some of the growing and developing that she could have otherwise done during that time. If this happens too often, then her body will not grow as tall as it could and her mind will not grow as sharp as it could. When this process is repeated for tens of millions of babies, a country's children do not learn as much as they could. They grow into a workforce that does not earn and produce as much as it could. The damage done to little babies can grow into big economic consequences.

In Chapter 5, we met Arun and Anil, two boys born at the same time in neighbouring villages, divided by the environment to which they were exposed in early life. By the time of Diane's post-Holi visit, Arun was 9 centimetres taller than Anil.

Anil and Arun also diverged cognitively. As Diane pulled each object from the bag, Arun promptly recited the names of almost all of them. His aunts, mother and grandmother all crowded between the brick wall and the double bed, eager to follow Diane's assessment of his progress. Arun quickly picked up the words that he did not already know, especially after his aunts and older cousins began quizzing him. If Diane asked 'What's the rope for?', he quickly replied 'To tie up a cow'. If she asked 'Which thing is for eating?', he handed her the spoon.

During the visit, Arun's mother slipped out of the room and returned wearing a pretty purple sari. Diane had apparently caught the family just before a big occasion. Arun piped up to explain that they were going to see his older brother, who was living at his maternal grandmother's house so that he could attend a better school. When Diane asked how they would get there, Arun said, 'On the motorcycle.' When she asked whose motorcycle it was, he proudly (if prematurely) announced, 'It's mine!'

The next day, Diane and Baby went to see Anil. They found his mother, dressed up in jewellery and a fancy sari, in the courtyard of her home. It is a typical village courtyard – the floor is a levelled surface of mud and cow dung, surrounded by short walls made of the same material.

Anil too was sitting in the courtyard, wearing clean new clothes that his mother had dressed him in for a puja ceremony. Anil looked far healthier than other times Diane had seen him. His nose was clean, not runny. His hair looked black, rather than the brownish hint of malnutrition. This time, there were no sores or pimples on his skin.

Despite his improved appearance, three-year-old Anil did not say anything. He was not just being shy – he could not yet speak. His mother said that Anil had recently started using baby words for 'mother' and 'father' that healthy children would normally start to say around their first birthday. He had also said 'bua' to get his aunts' attention a couple of times – but not more than twice or thrice, his buas emphasized.

The women in the village talk about Diane's visits. Diane did not want Anil's mother later to feel left out of the fun of discovering what was in the bag when she heard about the test from other families. So, one by one, Diane pulled out the objects and placed them in front of Anil. In the way a much younger baby might, he picked up the pen and started to make noise by tapping it against the steel container. The divergence in the health of Anil and Arun had become cognitive divergence too.

The economics of human capital

Economics is not only the study of money and prices any more. A generation or two ago, economics was best known for its theories: models of rational firms and families, maximizing their self-interest. When economists are in the news these days, it is typically for their *empirical* research: for using statistics to say something new about the world. The world has changed and economics has changed with it. A big part of what has made the difference is inexpensive computing power. Some of the empirical economics that is recognized with the Nobel Prize today was painstakingly researched decades ago using computers less powerful than today's telephones.

New data sources have also made new evidence available to answer old questions. Statistical surveys of health and well-being that barely existed in developing countries thirty or forty years ago are commonplace today. One consequence of all this empiricism is that academic boundaries are increasingly fuzzy. Today, there are economists who are more likely to write about the growth of babies than the growth of the bond market, separated from other researchers largely by economists' signature statistical methods. Yet, two features that still distinguish economists from other health researchers are that they are likely also to measure the educational and labour market consequences of health and that they insist on discussing it in apparently offensive language.

When economists write about health they often use the awkward phrase 'human capital', which seems to make babies equivalent to assets or machines. The concept of human capital was popularized by Chicago economist Gary Becker in the 1960s, who was emphasizing the value of investing in education. Indian families think about human capital too: They wonder whether their kids are going to study further in school than they did, whether they will make more money, and whether they will live in nicer houses and eat better food. But in university seminar rooms, the oxymoron of human capital symbolizes other academic disciplines' criticism of economists and their rational maths. After all, people are not backhoes or tractors, and humans should not be bought or sold like stocks or bonds. We should care when thousands of babies needlessly die, whether or not taking action would be a good financial investment.

All true. But beneath the apparently distasteful surface of 'human capital' is a solid fact, one that matters for the well-being of the poor: We humans need our bodies, and our bodies do not forget where they came from. What happens to us when we are babies – the health and nutrition we experience in utero and in our first months – endures in health and economic consequences for the rest of our lives. Ironically, this old theoretical label now motivates some of the leading empirical research of today, precisely because of the lasting import of early-life conditions that is so clear in the new statistical data available to modern researchers.

Early-life health may be an especially crucial form of capital for the world's poor, who are most likely to miss out on a good start, and who subsequently lack the resources for life's second chances. This means that in developing economies, studying health turns out to be studying money, prices and wages, after all. So, one important measure of the economic health of a country is the health of its babies. By moving beyond the familiar GDP, poverty and savings rates, economists have ultimately learnt that infant mortality and child height deserved a place among the important economic indicators all along.

The new 'growth' economics: Human height

In the new empirical economics of human capital, the height of our physical bodies has emerged as an especially important measure. Researchers noticed long ago that taller people tend to earn more money. Competing theories debated why. Some economists suggested that the labour market returns to height reflect physical strength. But, this could not explain the economic advantage of taller white-collar workers over their shorter office colleagues in rich countries. In 2007, Princeton economists Anne Case and Christina Paxson published evidence for one important explanation for the higher wages of taller people. In short, taller people are smarter, on average.

The 'on average' is a crucial part of that sentence. This is a fact about the statistics of populations, not comparisons across people. When babies and children are growing, it is not only their bodies that are getting larger and stronger: their brains are also developing. Many of the same chronic deficits or bad episodes of health that can keep a child from growing as tall as possible will also keep its cognitive ability from growing to its full potential. Of course, early-life health is not the only thing that matters to height. Within a population, different people inherit different genetic potential heights. Such genetic potentials are a large part of the difference between your height and the heights of the other people you will see today.

If all children were healthy and well fed and born to equally healthy and well-fed mothers, these genetic potentials would be the only reason that different people have different heights. But all children are not equally healthy and well fed. Thus, comparing across populations, differences in genetics average out, so average height is an indicator of the health and nutrition of babies. For the exact same reasons, height is a correlate of a person's eventual cognitive attainment.

So, taller children become taller adults. Taller children are smarter children who become smarter adults. Smarter adults are paid more. And all of this is true on average – not for every comparison between two people. Case and Paxson found that the difference in cognitive test scores between taller and shorter children can explain a large fraction of the difference in earnings that those same children receive when they grow up to be taller and shorter adults. Other researchers have shown similar effects in other countries. For example, economist Tom Vogl studied labour market outcomes among Mexican men. Like elsewhere, taller Mexican men earn more than shorter Mexican men, on average. Vogl's data also allows him to know what sort of job a worker has found: Is the worker more of a physical labourer or more of a thinker at a desk? 'Taller workers obtain more education,' Vogl concluded, ' and sort into occupations with greater intelligence requirements and lower strength requirements.'

———

Case and Paxson showed that taller children in the United States score better on learning tests, on average. We wondered if this would also be true in India, where a deeper threat of disease and malnutrition can knock children further off a course of healthy growth. Dean plotted comparable reading scores against height for a representative sample of American children and for a sample of Indian children.

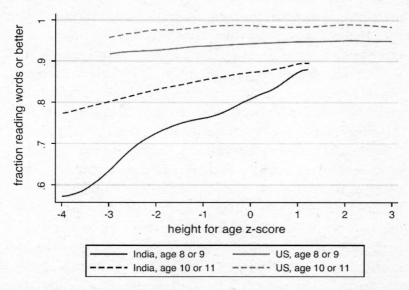

Figure 7. *Within India, taller children are much more likely to be able to read than shorter children*

In Figure 7, the horizontal axis is a child's height relative to a healthy reference population: Zero is average among healthy children of the same age. The curves for India are shifted relatively to the left into negative height numbers because most children there are too short. The vertical axis is a measure of reading ability, matched to be comparable across the tests used in India and the US. The unfortunate conclusion is visible in the slopes which track the average association between height and child learning: As important as the US correlation between height and cognitive achievement has been to economics researchers, the grey curves for the US are visibly much flatter than the black lines for India.

Shorter children in India are profoundly less likely to be able to read or work simple maths problems than their taller neighbours. The association between height and child learning in India is so steep that the correlation among American children is all but imperceptible when data from the two countries are placed side by side. The tallest US eight- or nine-year-olds are about 5 percentage points more likely to be able to recognize simple words than the shortest American children. In India, the same difference in height corresponds to a 20-percentage-point difference in the ability to read words.

So, height is steeply associated with cognitive achievement in a developing country such as India. This fact begins to point us towards the importance of babies' human capital. If height is especially important for what children learn, early-life health too is. Recall that differences in height reflect both differences in genetics and differences in the health and nutrition of young children. But, genetic differences would not cause height and cognitive achievement to be correlated; the correlation is a product of children's environments. This means that environments, healthy or unhealthy, are a large part of the variation across children in India. Human capital begins to accumulate – or fails to – even before children turn two years old.

Open defecation threatens children's ability to learn

In the last chapter, we saw that open defecation makes children shorter. On average, taller children learn more and are able to achieve more on tests. Open defecation and child stunting are both especially common in India. So, there is every reason to suspect that exposure to open defecation could threaten children's cognitive achievement. Could such an effect be detectable in data, and how important would the effect be?

Tracing the statistical path from a cause to an effect is always difficult. Many factors influence how much school-age children have been able to learn by the time they are old enough to take tests – their family's wealth, their parents' education, their educational opportunities, the motivation that they bring to their studies and heritable variation are only a few of the determinants that come immediately to mind. In order to look for an effect of exposure to open defecation on child learning, it would not be enough simply to compare test scores among children who lived amidst better and worse sanitation.

Any convincing statistical strategy would need two special features. First, the researcher would have to know something special about why some children were exposed to more open defecation than others. If differences in exposure to open defecation reflected differences in the wealth or education of their communities, there would be no hope of disentangling the effect of sanitation from other effects of poverty or literacy. To truly identify the influence of sanitation, we would want a special situation in which open defecation suddenly changed but other factors stayed the same. In India, this is a tall order. We are writing this book precisely because open defecation has declined only very slowly. Moreover, if the situation is really all that special, we might question whether we can really learn anything from it that can usefully apply to other cases.

The second challenge is timing. By the time a child is old enough to go to school and take maths and reading tests, much of her developmental trajectory is set. Height at two years of age is already highly predictive of height as an adult. This means that what we care about is the relationship between a child's achievement *when she is in school* and her exposure to open defecation *when she was a baby*. Measuring that relationship would require matching two sources of data: one on early-life exposure to open defecation and another on later-childhood achievement.

This does not necessarily mean that exposure to open defecation does not matter at all for a child's success once she is old enough to go to school. One obvious risk is that children who fall ill more frequently are more likely to miss classes! More subtly, as we saw in the previous chapter, exposure to open defecation might contribute to anaemia, which saps a child's energy and makes it more difficult to concentrate on studies. Parasites too can harm school-age children.

Economist Hoyt Bleakley studied a hookworm eradication campaign of the Rockefeller Sanitary Commission in the US South during the early twentieth century. Because different places suffered different levels of hookworm infection to begin with, when the deworming campaign began some places experienced larger improvements than others. Most people in North Carolina were infected with hookworm before the programme, so it benefited from a large decline in hookworm infection; Alabama had lower initial rates of infection, so there was not as much room for an equally large improvement. Bleakley found that 'areas with higher levels of hookworm infection prior to the [campaign] experienced greater increases in school enrollment, attendance, and literacy after the intervention'. Places where hookworm infections fell more sharply turned out to be places where schooling improved by more. Years later, as these children grew, incomes did too.

Some of the effects that Bleakley found in the US South probably happened because healthier babies attained greater cognitive development; some of the effects were probably because healthier school-age children were better able to attend and concentrate at school. Without denying the importance of the second mechanism, we have been focusing on the first: the human capital that healthy babies accumulate. Does infants' exposure to open defecation shape their subsequent learning in India? Are six-year-olds still suffering from the diarrhoea they had as babies – not just physically but also cognitively?

Children bring their neighbours' toilets to school

Bleakley found a useful special case that careful statistical analysis could learn from. Could a similar special case reveal an effect of open defecation on child learning in India? Dean and a fellow researcher Sneha Lamba used variation in a government sanitation programme to get past these statistical challenges. The Total Sanitation Campaign (TSC) was a programme of the Indian government in the 2000s. The TSC made modest improvements in sanitation that caused a moderate reduction in open defecation. As we will see in the later chapters of this book, the TSC was not the last word in sanitation in India: Although it caused some improvements, it was by no means perfect. Seventy per cent of rural households did not own a latrine when the campaign ended. Open defecation decreased by only about 10 percentage points over the ten-year span of the TSC. However, open defecation is bad enough for children's health that even this improvement in sanitation caused meaningful, statistically detectable improvements in early-life health.

In order to measure effects of improvements in open defecation on children's cognitive development and, later, test scores, Sneha and Dean looked closely at how the TSC started. The implementation of the TSC did not begin in all districts throughout India at the same time. Children who were born in districts where the TSC was first implemented would have started life exposed to a little bit less open defecation than children born in the same district a year or two earlier. In contrast, children who were born in other districts, with a later start to the TSC, would be exposed to about the same sanitation as children born in the same place the year before. If, six years later, learning in exposed and unexposed districts evolved differently over time, this could be evidence for a role of sanitation in cognitive development.

The last necessary piece was a measure of child learning. The Hindi word 'aser' means 'an effect' or 'an influence'. Appropriately, the ASER survey is a nationwide effort by the non-profit organization Pratham to produce an Annual Status of Education Report each year. The survey deploys 30,000 volunteers throughout India, reaching villages in every district. Surveyors give children simple tests of reading, writing and maths. Since 2005, these tests have lived up to their acronym, publicly highlighting profound gaps in learning – even among children who are enrolled in school. Sneha and Dean matched the ASER test scores in each year and in each district with records of the roll-out of the TSC six years earlier.

Children exposed to less open defecation in the environment into which they were born scored better, on average, on the ASER tests of learning achievement. Exposure to the TSC increased the fraction of rural six-year-olds who would recognize letters by about three-tenths of a percentage point. Results were similar for a test of whether children could recognize numbers.

As a fraction of India's overall learning deficit, three-tenths of a percentage point is a small effect, especially on any one child. This is no surprise: The TSC did not convince most rural Indians to stop defecating in the open. But this small average effect is important because it accumulates over many, many children. Further, the fact that these results are statistically detectable at all – among the wide variation in test scores and their many determinants – emphasizes that open defecation is a way in which children in India become cognitively stunted. We can hope that the positive effect on learning would be much larger for the major reduction in open defecation that India may someday achieve.

Lest any reader misunderstand our point, open defecation is only one of many constraints that prevent Indian children from achieving all the human capital that would be possible for them. Many children unfortunately learn little despite sitting through many days of schooling, falling ever further behind the curriculum. Economist Karthik Muralidharan explains that the entire objective of the Indian educational system may be misplaced: Through testing and screening, the goal of the system appears to be only to identify the most talented students, not to promote the learning and skills of all citizens. On this view, schooling in India functions in practice only as a filter. Accelerating the decline of open defecation would not solve this problem. But as education in India improves, or perhaps especially as it does not, the evidence on early-life human capital suggests that children will achieve more when they enter school with bodies and brains that are ready to learn.

What doesn't kill you makes you poorer

We have often been surprised to learn how harmful open defecation can be. But economics research is not always surprising: Some of the most important research carefully and progressively reach a better understanding of situations that are significant but intuitive. Much of the modern statistical practice of economists, for example, was forged in article after article documenting ever more precisely the extent to which better educated people are paid more.

A growing set of studies can link childhood exposure to disease to adult economic outcomes in developing countries. Two recent papers, both investigating consequences of exposure to malaria, were published together in the same issue of a leading journal of applied economics. One study, by David Cutler and co-authors, investigated the economic consequences for adults of exposure in early childhood to a malaria eradication programme in India in the 1950s. The other, by Hoyt Bleakley, uses malaria eradication campaigns conducted in the 1920s in the United States and in 1950s in Latin America to identify effects of child exposure on adult labour productivity. Both studies found lasting effects of malaria from decades earlier.

To review: We have seen that open defecation makes children shorter; that shorter children perform worse on cognitive tests; and that reducing open defecation can improve child learning. In other countries and other situations, economists have detected effects of early-life health and disease on adult earnings. All this evidence points in the same direction: Early-life exposure to open defecation is likely to reduce the productivity of adult workers and impact the wages they earn. After all the surprises among the facts of open defecation, it would be no surprise if this existing research on early-life capital extended to sanitation too.

Existing research told us to expect an effect of sanitation on wages in India.

But quantitatively, how big should we expect the effect to be? To answer this question, Dean recruited the collaboration of Nicholas Lawson, now an economics professor at the University of Quebec at Montreal. Nicholas is a labour economist whose research is dedicated to careful quantitative assessments of how best to improve social safety net programmes for workers and their families. Nicholas came to visit Dean in Delhi and in Uttar Pradesh, and together they made a plan to learn about the extent to which childhood exposure to open defecation reduces the wages of adults.

It is not enough to compare workers who were born in places with bad disease environments with workers who were born in places with good disease environments, and merely see if they earn different wages. If their wages differed, it could be because of open defecation. But it also could be because of any number of other differences. Perhaps the labour markets are different – meaning that there are simply more jobs available in places where open defecation was more common. Or perhaps workers in places with less open defecation attended less school. Or perhaps the two places tend to be home to people assigned a different rank in the caste hierarchy. Any of these factors – and more – could make a simple comparison misleading.

Part of a solution is to compare workers who were, in principle, competing against one another for similar jobs but who were exposed to different levels of open defecation in their early years. Most people in India work in the same district where they live. So, Nicholas and Dean decided to compare workers within districts. Studying workers exposed to different early-life conditions within the same district would hold much of their labour markets constant.

Figure 8 is computed using the data from Nicholas and Dean's research. It presents a basic fact of labour economics: Older workers are typically paid more than younger workers. If you draw a graph of average wages for workers at each age, the line almost always slopes up, and India is no exception. This slope is usually attributed to the fact that older workers have accumulated experience that employers are willing to pay more for. But, in some places the line slopes up more steeply (meaning older workers are paid much more than younger workers), and in some places the line slopes up more gradually (meaning younger workers are earning almost as much as older workers).

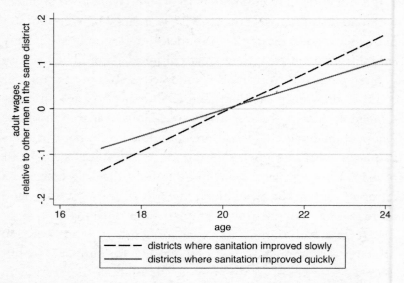

Figure 8. In places where open defecation has improved more quickly, younger workers earn more relative to older workers

Throughout India, early-life health has been improving. Open defecation rates are declining; each year, a larger fraction of infants survive to their first birthday; and evidence suggests that children are getting slightly taller as time goes on. We are writing this book primarily because these improvements have been so much slower than in other countries, and because we hope that they can be accelerated. But even within India, there are differences: In some districts, open defecation has been declining more quickly, and in others, more slowly.

Nicholas and Dean found a research strategy that combined these two facts: That older workers tend to be paid more than younger workers and that open defecation has been declining more quickly in some districts than in others. Where open defecation has been falling relatively fast, younger workers grew up in a much healthier environment than older workers. Where open defecation has been falling slowly, younger and older workers would have been born into relatively similar disease environments.

This research strategy is visible in Figure 8, which splits the data into districts where open defecation has fallen relatively quickly and districts where it has fallen only slowly. If open defecation matters for adult wages, the relationship between ages and wages should be different in districts where open defecation has fallen more quickly, compared with districts where open defecation has fallen more slowly. Experience should count as an advantage for older workers everywhere, but it would be partially outweighed by better early-life health in districts where disease has fallen quickly.

So, this was the approach: Nicholas and Dean asked whether the wage gap between older workers and younger workers is, on average, smaller in districts where the early-life disease environment has been improving more quickly. In particular, they matched wage information from each adult male worker, in a nationwide survey from 2005, with data on the fraction of households that practised open defecation from the district and year of his birth. They also used historical data on infant mortality rates to double-check that open defecation appropriately captured the disease environment. This strategy ensured that their results did not merely misleadingly reflect the fact that workers of different ages or in different districts earn different wages, and that they always compared workers competing for jobs within the same district-wide labour market.

When Nicholas and Dean had computed their results, the three of us travelled together to a conference at the University of Allahabad. Nicholas started his presentation where our thinking on this project began: He drew a picture of a web. Nicholas's web was a reminder of how much we had learnt from other economists' research and how thoroughly this project built upon other findings that had come before. Each node in the web was a stage in a worker's life and a measure of his human capital: his adult height, his childhood height, his childhood cognition, his adult wages and his early-life health. Each of these nodes had been connected by earlier studies of workers – each pair of nodes, that is – but one: no line connected early-life sanitation to adult earnings. The dense web offered every reason to expect to find an effect of open defecation on adult wages – but would it appear in the data?

It did. Each additional reduction in the open defecation level to which a worker was exposed to as a baby translated into a small percentage increase in his adult wages. We can see this result in Figure 8, in the difference in the slope between the two lines: Younger workers are less disadvantaged, relative to older workers, in districts where they have benefited from improved sanitation. That is, the gradient between age and wages in these districts is less steep.

The effect on any one worker would be relatively small, but it adds up to something substantial in the population. Yet again, what matters is how many people in a person's neighbourhood defecate in the open, not whether the person himself uses a toilet. Even children whose families own and use a toilet will grow up to suffer the economic consequences of their neighbours' open defecation.

Does nutrition trap Indians in poverty?

There is a long-standing theory that poor health and poor nutrition might limit the ability of poor people to earn money. So far in this chapter, we have emphasized the losses in learning and productivity in survivors of early-life disease and poor nutrition. But economists used to theorize about an entirely different type of 'nutritional poverty trap'. It used to be common to claim that poor people cannot earn money because they cannot work, and they cannot work because they simply cannot afford enough food to do manual labour. If this were true, poverty itself would keep poor people poor. Poor nutrition would trap the poor in poverty, through no fault of their own.

Such a nutritional poverty trap would be different from the stories of human capital that we have been telling. The evidence that we have been discussing points to an important role of health and nutrition in childhood: What happens to babies shapes their bodies' development in ways that have lasting implications. The older ideas about a nutritional poverty trap, in contrast, proposed that nutrition constrains poor workers *as adults*. Might labourers be trapped in poverty merely because they are too poor to buy the food energy needed to work?

Shankar Subramanian and Angus Deaton investigated this possibility in 1996 using data from rural Maharashtra. They indeed found that richer people do eat more: An average household that doubled its income might eat 30 per cent to 50 per cent more calories. But they also found that calories are cheap in rural Maharashtra – food is just not expensive enough for the simple theory of a nutritional poverty trap of working adults' energy to be true. The extra 600 calories that might be needed to spend a day doing physical work (rather than less remunerative, more leisurely activity) would cost only about 4 per cent of the daily wage.

Of course, even if food does not cause this type of poverty trap, it would not imply that hunger is never an important policy issue, nor that there is no compelling public reason to care about food security or maternal nutrition. Better-fed children can better concentrate in school; better schooling has positive external benefits for everyone, which is one reason why so many countries have programmes to feed poor children at school. Moreover, the fact that older theories of adult-nutrition poverty traps are not supported by the evidence does not imply that newer theories of child-nutrition poverty traps are false. Rather, it reminds us that these are separate ideas, about what happens at separate stages of life. In the new 'growth' economics, age matters, and investments in human capital can have the biggest returns for the youngest children.

Why are Indians eating fewer calories than they used to?

When Deaton and Subramanian confirmed that richer households tend to eat more, they were verifying Engel's law, one of the oldest established facts in economics. Engel's law is named for Ernst Engel, a nineteenth-century economist and statistician from Germany. The law holds that richer households spend more money on food than poorer households, but that they also spend a lower proportion of their total budgets on food. So, the poorest families might spend one-third of their incomes on food; while richer families would spend a higher total amount on food, as a fraction it might only be, perhaps, one-fifth of their total incomes.

Engel's historical law still holds in India today: Richer Indians in 2016 consumed more calories than poorer Indians in 2016, on average. This fact is certainly predictable, but it is part of yet another unpredictable Indian nutritional puzzle, documented by Angus Deaton and Indian economist Jean Drèze: Average calorie intake in India has been declining since the 1980s. Using data from the National Sample Survey (NSS) they computed that, in 1983, the average person in rural India ate 2,240 calories per day. By 2005, this fell by almost 200 calories to 2,047 calories per person per day. How could it be that a poor population, upon becoming richer, is eating less?

Dean wondered if disease might also play a part in this nutritional puzzle, and collaborated with economist Josephine Duh to find out. Jo is an expert at the complex NSS survey data, which has recorded food consumption among Indian households since the 1980s. Although open defecation has not been falling as fast as we might like it to, it has been declining. If people in India are not exposed to as much disease as they used to be, their intestines will be healthier and be better able to absorb the food they eat. If the average family in India is exposed to a little less intestinal disease today than in the 1980s, they might be able to afford to eat fewer calories and save that part of their food budget for something else that they want to buy.

Jo and Dean found evidence for this idea in three different Indian data sources. They used two measures of the disease environment: open defecation and infant mortality. First, and most importantly, districts in India where infant mortality has been falling the most quickly over recent decades – that is, the districts with the fastest improvements – are, on average, also the districts where calorie consumption has declined the most. Second, people living in Indian villages with more open defecation or greater local infant mortality rates also ate more calories, on average. In particular, people eat more, on average, in villages where children suffer more diarrhoea, but fever and cough (other common childhood symptoms that do not reflect *intestinal* disease) are unrelated to food consumption. Finally, a unique survey from the 1980s measured calorie consumption, local open defecation and a detailed description of the work a household does. This data can verify that the relationship between disease and calorie consumption is not merely a misleading consequence of poor people working in more demanding jobs for which they need to eat more food.

One of the three data sources, the India Human Development Survey, also measured the heights and weights of adult Indian women. This physical data presents an opportunity to check the plausibility of Jo and Dean's findings. If open defecation causes diseases that decrease the absorption of food, does it make people thinner? Richer women in India weigh more than poorer women in India, but household calorie consumption – which turns out to be only one part of the net nutritional equation, and which may tell us little about what individual women within the household eat – is not strongly associated with women's body mass. Yet, on the role of disease, the data is clear: Across the range of rich and poor, and among households eating many calories or fewer calories, women surrounded by a larger fraction of neighbours defecating in the open weigh less than women facing less environmental disease.

With all this data, Jo and Dean returned to the puzzling decline in calorie consumption in India. Could a slowly improving disease environment account for the decline, over time, in calorie intake? Yes, but only partially. Different approaches to computing the role of disease give slightly different answers. However, it seems clear that disease can explain some of the calorie decline, although not all of it. Jo and Dean think that a rough lower bound is that gradual improvements in disease can explain about a quarter of the decline, possibly more.

These results leave some open puzzles. First, if improvements in the disease environment caused a quarter of the decline in calorie consumption, what caused the rest? Maybe, as Deaton and Drèze suggest, improvements in technology and infrastructure, like tractors and roads, have decreased people's activity levels in ways that allow them to maintain their weight while consuming fewer calories. If so, this process should also be found in other developing countries, even where they have never recently had similarly threatening levels of open defecation.

Second, even if a reduced disease burden makes people effectively 'richer' in calories, why are people who are so unhealthily thin not using that extra food budget to get a little fatter? In 2005, India had a higher fraction of underweight women than any country in the Demographic and Health Surveys besides Eritrea, which has been plagued by poverty and war. Diane has documented that pregnant women in India fare especially poorly: She estimated that in 2005 over 40 per cent of Indian women began pregnancy underweight. And it is not just women who are unhealthily thin: In the same survey, a quarter of Indian men aged between forty and fifty were underweight as well.

Despite these open puzzles, Dean and Jo's results suggest that open defecation wastes a little bit of India's food each day. Because people with intestinal diseases cannot absorb all of the food that they eat, many people purchase, cook and consume more calories than they would otherwise need to. Although the effect of open defecation on any one household's food budget is typically small, these small effects add up over a large population. If Jo and Dean's estimates are approximately correct, eliminating open defecation would save the average person in India about 50 calories per day. For example, if a person at the World Bank's international poverty line spends a third of his income on 2,000 calories, the least expensive calories in India might cost two-hundredths of one penny. In this case, eliminating open defecation would save an average of three to four dollars per person per year in wasted food energy. These few dollars would not break India's bank, but they would add up to a total annual cost of around 10 per cent to 20 per cent of the annual spending of the Indian government on the public distribution of food.

How open defecation taxes the government's budget

Some critics claim that the Indian government spends too much money on its public distribution system for food. We have seen that if people's bodies were better able to absorb and use the food they ate, perhaps government spending on nutrition could get more returns to the rupee. But we tend to object when people use our research to argue against subsidized food: Whatever the benefits and costs of food subsidies, sanitation is a small part of that equation and wasted food is a small part of why sanitation matters to India's economy. The big economic effects of open defecation accrue to survivors, years after the diseases of childhood. We have seen in this chapter that poor sanitation today lowers child cognitive achievement in a few years and reduces the wages of adult workers in a few decades. If workers are earning less money, families are paying less in taxes. Could all of this amount to a meaningful effect on government revenues?

Recall Nicholas Lawson, the labour economist who helped compute the effect of sanitation on wages. His particular speciality is to build computer simulations of government policies that apply estimates of the size of economic effects – such as the effect of childhood exposure to open defecation. He constructs estimates to provide quantitative advice to government policymakers. How large should a tax be? How much money should unemployed Canadians receive in social insurance? How fully should public colleges be subsidized?

In this case, Nicholas asked just how much a hypothetically stingy Indian government should be willing to spend to reduce open defecation – assuming the government only cares about its own revenues and not the well-being of its citizens. Because lower open defecation will one day mean higher wages, and, therefore, larger incomes, more spending and more sales tax, spending money to reduce open defecation now would lead to larger government revenues in the future through consumption taxes. If the government could eliminate open defecation now, it would be able to collect more money in taxes in the future. But how much revenue more would the government stand to gain?

The extra revenue in the government treasury would not start appearing for about twenty years, because a better disease environment will only turn into higher wages and more spending when today's babies have grown into tomorrow's workers. So, government accountants would have to discount the extra future tax revenue before considering how much the government should spend on sanitation today. How many rupees, in twenty-five years, are worth the same to the government as one rupee spent today? One reasonable answer is to use the actual interest rate that the government of India pays when it borrows money. This is what Nicholas did.

The result? Even if the government spent approximately 25,000 rupees to cause a family to switch from open defecation to latrine use, the government itself would make money from this sanitation programme! In other words, reducing open defecation would be (so slightly) beneficial to (so many) people's wages that the government would eventually increase its own revenues by an amount worth about the same to the government as receiving 25,000 rupees today. It would receive this for every household it can cause to stop defecating in the open today. This would be enough money to pay for a serious behaviour change campaign or (at least in principle) enough even to buy each household a large underground tank.

What is striking about this computation is that it ignores all benefits of reducing open defecation besides the increase in taxes from higher wages. It does not, for instance, take into account the benefits to parents who do not have to experience an infant death, or higher consumption for the families of workers who earn more, or reduced public and private medical expenses or even the effect on food consumption. If this figure is approximately correct, even a perfectly greedy government that cares only for its own revenues might find it maximizing its profits by tackling open defecation effectively. Yet, the flip side of these results is that tackling open defecation *ineffectively* is a double waste of the government's budget: It wastes the money spent on misguided programmes today and wastes the opportunity to take in more revenue in the future.

───

The economic effects of open defecation touch every taxpayer: It creates a toxic disease environment, which, in densely populated India, often plagues even the wealthy. But even people who never fall ill must pay enough tax to balance a government budget that all Indians share. Industrialists must select among workers for hire who grew up surrounded by neighbours who did not use latrines. Another bad economic consequence of open defecation may be that it also contributes to India's wide inequality. The average household among the richest 20 per cent of Indian households is exposed to 16 per cent of its neighbours defecating in the open. In contrast, among the poorest 20 per cent of households in India, 86 per cent of their neighbours defecate in the open. This unequal exposure to open defecation is a source of further inequality in both health and income. It contributes to the perpetuation of inequality across generations. Applying Dean and Nicholas's estimates of the effect of sanitation on adult wages, if no other differences reinforce or counteract its effect, the difference in exposure to open defecation would cause boys born in the poorest quintile of Indian households to grow up to earn about 10 per cent less than boys born in the richest quintile of Indian households. This figure is approximate, and sanitation is of course only a small part of India's inequality. Still, open defecation is among the forces causing illness to be correlated with poverty in India, making inequality across people's overall well-being worse than it would be if only money or health were considered.

If the government could reduce open defecation, it would make economic sense to do so. If all of this sounds to you like a good argument for the public construction of free latrines for every family in India, you are not alone. Unfortunately, as we saw in the first part of the book, this perfectly reasonable economic conclusion may only waste even more money, depending on whether it is part of a broader rural sanitation package. Yet, government after government in Delhi has attempted essentially the same latrine construction programme, with very little reduction in open defecation rates. So, in the final part of the book, we will ask why: Why has the policy response to open defecation not moved beyond construction of subsidized latrines?

7 | Dignity: The people who want latrines

In May 2014, the deaths of two girls in a village in Badaun, a district in Uttar Pradesh, made national and international headlines. The media reported that the girls, who were found hanging from a mango tree, had been raped and murdered while defecating in the open. Prominent journalists and public figures called for an end to open defecation on the grounds that it would protect women. A well-known social service organization pledged to build latrines for every household in the girls' village. United Nations Secretary-General Ban Ki-moon said, 'I was especially appalled by the brutal rape and gruesome murder of two teenaged women in India, who had ventured out because they did not have access to a toilet.'

A later CBI investigation found that the girls were not raped or murdered, but that they had committed suicide after one of the girls was caught having an intimate relationship with a young man from the village and the other was caught helping her cover it up. The *Indian Express* quoted a CBI official who explained that going to defecate in the open had merely been the girls' unobjectionable excuse to leave the house and meet the young man. To be sure, the CBI's investigation has not been universally accepted; it is likely that people who were not present will never know the whole story.

As important as this case is in its own right, we share the story here because, whatever happened, it revealed the assumptions of journalists, government officials and development professionals who misunderstand how most rural men and women view open defecation. As we have seen in earlier chapters, open defecation is not an activity that most people are 'forced' into due to lack of latrines, but rather one that most household decision makers chose over using the kinds of affordable latrines that would need to be emptied manually. We have considered the question of whether policymakers should even work to reduce open defecation, considering that it is freely chosen by many villagers, that it is unclear who would empty latrine pits when they fill up – and that the need for someone to empty full latrine pits would possibly harm Dalits' struggle for equality.

Yet, in the last two chapters, we met infants and children who are made irreversibly worse off by open defecation and who would probably vote for their neighbours to use latrines if they could vote on such a policy. In this chapter, we will meet a different group of people who suffer from India's widespread open defecation for a different reason. They are the elderly, the disabled and those young women whose families allow them to leave the house to defecate only in the dark or under strict supervision.

Unlike for their healthier, more mobile family members, open defecation is often a burdensome experience for these people. Unfortunately, the common alternative to open defecation – defecating on the ground in the house or courtyard, as small children do – can be humiliating. The fact that purity and pollution rules, and the renegotiation of untouchability, have made affordable latrines socially unacceptable causes many elderly and disabled people, and some young women, to suffer needlessly.

In this chapter, we first examine women's attitudes towards open defecation. Our qualitative fieldwork, supported by data from the SQUAT survey, finds that rural women are not always as opposed to open defecation as city people assume them to be. After all, rural women live in a society that has broadly positive attitudes towards the practice. When the SQUAT survey asked open-ended questions in which men and women volunteered their explanations of what is good or bad about open defecation, about half of the people said that they defecate in the open because it is pleasurable, comfortable or convenient. Among individuals who defecate in the open despite having access to a latrine, about three quarters said that it was pleasurable, comfortable or convenient.

Although the SQUAT survey found that women are more likely to use available latrines than men, this fact may reflect constraints on women's movement rather than women's own preferences. We can only conclude that a behaviour reveals a person's preference if we have good reason to believe that the behaviour is freely chosen. But little in the lives of young women in rural India is freely chosen. For many women in rural India, using a latrine is expected of them; for others, defecating in the open is unremarkably normal. Women of neither group are typically the household decision makers.

We then turn to the hardship and humiliation of people who are too old or crippled to walk to the fields or the forest. They face a dilemma: Because latrines are socially construed to be necessarily expensive, reserved for the rich, they must either burden their families with the cost of a latrine or burden family members with the task of removing their faeces from the home or angan (courtyard). Providing subsidized latrines for this minority of rural Indians would do little to improve the disease environment caused by open defecation – where we have seen latrines built for this reason are not often used by other family members – but they would make these people's lives better.

Women and open defecation

The media coverage of the Badaun case reveals that many urban people assume that open defecation is burdensome, embarrassing and even dangerous for rural women. Urbanites further assume that if women got to make financial decisions, they would be far more likely than men to invest in latrines.

There is some truth to these assumptions, but it is a complicated truth. Many people who invoke the consequences of latrine 'access' do not realize how inexpensive a functional latrine can be. Nor do they realize how broadly positive villagers' attitudes towards open defecation are. Both men and women speak openly about the benefits of open defecation and even associate it with health and longevity.

In conversations about open defecation, many villagers contrast village life with city life. They often imagine Indian cities to be dirty, crowded places where there is no space to take a walk and defecate in the open; they believe that village air is healthier than city air and that it has healing properties. Some people even express pity for city people who are not able to enjoy the benefits open defecation.

An higher-caste man whom we interviewed had built a latrine for his new daughter-in-law from the city, but said that he did not use it himself. He explained, '*Shaher ka dava, dihat ka hava*!' He was saying that while people in cities take medicine when they are sick, villagers rely on the fresh air to cure what ails them.

In another interview, Diane and Nikhil spoke with a middle-aged woman in Haryana who owned a latrine. She was the head of her household because her husband was suffering from mental illness and her mother-in-law was elderly and disabled. She got a latrine built in the courtyard of their house because it was difficult for her husband and mother-in-law to walk far enough to defecate in the open. Nevertheless, she often defecates in the open herself.

Nikhil asked her why so many of the people in her village who own latrines defecate in the open. She explained, 'People say, I'll take a walk outside, so if there is any illness, it will [get better by being exposed to] the open air, don't you think? The stomach's fullness also reduces a bit, and walking also makes [blood flow in the veins] ... Brother, a person who can walk will go out [defecate] in the open; a person who cannot walk will remain on his cot.'

Still, as with almost every activity in gender-obsessed rural India, there are ways in which open defecation is different for women than it is for men. Men, particularly higher-caste Hindus, are more likely than women to stress the 'wholesomeness' of a morning routine that involves open defecation. Rising early, preferably before sunrise, taking a vigorous walk to the fields, defecating there and returning to bathe are all elements of a morning routine that promotes masculinity, bodily purity and virtue.

A young middle-caste man who does not own a latrine explained this mindset to us:

> People here do not use latrines. They say that we'll go early in the morning ... There are orchards, there are mango trees all around. When they go there early in the morning before sunrise, when they go to defecate early in the morning, at four in the morning, waking up at four in the morning, at four ... then getting up while it is still dark everyone gets some fresh air as well ... [In this village,]

some five to ten people have latrines but they do not use them, because only people who are sick and so are not able to go out and defecate in the open use latrines. Only in such a condition does a man use a latrine. Otherwise you should comfortably go, comfortably go and take in the clean outdoor environment, take in some fresh air, and then return home. Village men are strong because they work in the fields, and because there they also get fresh air. If you have a latrine, and a place for bathing, and you defecate in your house, and you do not take a walk anywhere, you do not get out, then you will have pains in your body.

Women are less likely to express views like this one, which associates open defecation with vigour and strength. After all, these are not characteristics associated with femininity.

The SQUAT survey found that, among people living in households that own a latrine, women were about 9 per cent more likely to use it than men. Does this mean that women want to use latrines more than men do? The answer to this question is complicated by the fact that much of women's behaviour in rural India is not freely chosen. There is no reason to assume that latrine use would be the only exception to the pattern of constraints that rural women face.

Women, and especially young women, are sometimes expected to defecate earlier in the morning than men, sometimes while it is still dark. This restriction is in no way unique to open defecation. Constraining women's behaviour and keeping them inside the home is one of the ways that a household that aspires to been seen as socially high-ranking demonstrates its propriety and status. This is evident in the fact that gender norms are typically more constraining for women in higher-caste households than in lower-caste households. In demographic survey data, for example, mothers in higher-caste families report having less authority in household decisions than mothers in Dalit families. Caste differences notwithstanding, only a minority of rural women, of any background, report getting to make decisions about when they travel, what they buy and how their children are cared for.

Attitudes and practices that constrain women's mobility and decision making make open defecation less convenient than it would be if young women were as free to come and go from the house as young men are. Thankfully, though, the majority of women who responded to the SQUAT survey were not required to defecate in the dark. Only 13 per cent of all women who defecate in the open, and only 18 per cent of women between eighteen and twenty-five who defecate in the open, reported having to do so in the dark. Understandably, when restrictions on what times of day women can defecate in the open are enforced, women are more interested in using latrines.

Similarly, in some households, young married women are not allowed to leave the house to defecate unless they are accompanied by another family member. As the lowest-ranking members of their households, they often have to wait for an appropriate chaperone to be available. In such cases too young women find latrines more convenient than open defecation.

But when they are allowed to defecate in the open as freely as men are, many rural women are not interested in using latrines. A young Muslim woman in Uttar Pradesh explained that by defecating in the open 'you can get some fresh air and some peace. If you're cooped up in the house all day, and then you go outside, your mind and body get refreshed.'

Considering how restricted the movement of women is in rural India, it was no surprise to us that many women reported enjoying the temporary freedom and sociality that open defecation provides. A young woman in Haryana reported being disappointed when her husband had built a latrine and expected her to use it. She missed the brief daily opportunity to get away from the house and to talk and laugh freely with the female friends who accompanied her to defecate in the open.

Women with less controlling relatives may choose not to use a latrine even if it is available. The older woman in Haryana whom we quoted above (who did not use her own latrine) has four young daughters-in-law who also opted for open defecation. One of them explained to us, 'The reason that we go outside [to defecate] is that we get to wander a bit ... you know, we live cooped up inside.'

———

Many men who owned latrines told us that they built them particularly for the young women in their households to use. These men were not generally as concerned with keeping others from seeing their young female relatives while defecating in the open as they were with preventing others from seeing the young women *at all*. Similarly, it may well be that women in rural India are vulnerable to harassment and assault while going to defecate outside merely because too many women in rural India are vulnerable to harassment and assault at all times.

Is open defecation an occasion when women are particularly vulnerable to sexual assault? Of 1,046 women whom we interviewed, 4.3 per cent told us that while going to defecate, they had been the victim of someone attempting to molest them. But, of the same group, 7.6 per cent reported that this had happened to them while going to the market. The point is not that these events are necessarily comparable or that these statistics have captured the full extent of violence against women. The point is that it is not a serious policy response to these facts to suggest that women should stop going to markets. Ending sexual violence, ending open defecation and ensuring social access to markets for everyone are all important goals, but they will not be resolved by the same public policy or programme.

The facts that many women in rural India face severe restrictions on their freedom of movement and that many women associate open defecation with freedom stand in stark contrast to the patriarchal messages that the government uses to encourage men to invest in latrines. One of the many slogans we have seen painted on village walls in several north Indian states reads in a rhyming rhythmic jingle: '*Bahu betiyon bahar na jaye, ghar me hi shauchalya banaye*!' 'Daughters-in-law and daughters should not go outside, make a toilet in your house!'

This message reinforces restrictions on women's movement and decision making – and not just about sanitation. This is not a useful idea for government messages to promote: The low social position of women in Indian society is already widely recognized as a major human development shortcoming. Patriarchal sanitation messages miss the important point that everyone who defecates in the open, not only women, spreads germs that make other people sick. Men – whose faeces also contain pathogens – are made no more likely to use latrines by signs announcing that toilets are for women.

The elderly, the disabled and expensive latrines

When Diane and Nidhi met Govind in his village in Haryana, he looked quite healthy for a sixty-five-year-old man. But we soon found out that a couple of years before he had been very sick, and that his illness had lasted for more than a year. He said that he had suffered from diabetes and tuberculosis.

When he was sick, it was hard for Govind to move around, and sometimes he even had trouble controlling his bowels. He hesitantly explained that before the latrine was built 'there were no arrangements. I used to go outside, right here…' By this he meant that he used to defecate in the angan of his home. His voice cracked as he tried to stop the tears in his eyes at the thought of that painful memory. His wife, Sonam, picked up where he had left off, explaining that he used to squat over a metal pan in the courtyard. Then, she or his daughter-in-law or their son would throw his faeces out in the fields.

Govind explained that because of this, he wanted to build a latrine. His wife had supported the idea but his son and daughter-in-law had not. When he recounted 'The children did not want the latrine, they said they didn't have the money for it', the tears that had been welling up in his eyes started flowing down his cheeks. He went on: 'So I said, I will pay for it, out of my own money.'

The latrine cost 20,000 rupees and had 5.5 metre-deep cylindrical pit that was lined with brick and cement.

We met many families like Govind's, who spent many times the cost of a latrine in Bangladesh or in sub-Saharan Africa to build a latrine with a large pit because an elderly or sick person was having trouble defecating in the open. Our interview with a young woman named Seema and her grandfather-in-law, whom she affectionately called 'Baba', was particularly memorable. Seema and her husband, Raj, had completed construction of the latrine only three days before we visited their village.

The latrine was decidedly out of place next to their house, made out of mud, cow dung and thatch; it was a large, brick-and-cement structure, with a cement-lined tank behind it. Seema knew that they could have built a pit latrine like the ones provided by the government and that it would have been far less expensive. But, she said, emptying such a pit would have been a problem. They were able to save money on labour costs though, because Raj is a mason. He and Seema built the latrine themselves.

Baba was clearly embarrassed by how much money Raj and Seema had spent on latrine parts. They were a poor family that had experienced much tragedy: Seema's first two children had died and Raj's younger brother had gone missing several years before when he left the village to work in another state as a migrant labourer. Yet, the fact that Baba had fallen down on his way to defecate in the open a few months before and had difficulty getting up seemed to convince him to accept Raj and Seema's gift of a latrine.

Not every elderly or disabled person is as lucky as Govind or Seema's Baba. In Govind's case, he had enough of his own money to make his own latrine, and Seema's Baba had a close relationship with grandchildren who were willing and able to build the latrine for him. But for every rural household that has built a latrine for a family member who desperately needs it, there are many more in which old and disabled people suffer the daily humiliation of either hobbling painfully to the fields or of having someone else clean up and dispose of their faeces. We remember meeting a young Dalit woman in Uttar Pradesh who was unable to walk upright because she had polio. She manoeuvred slowly on her hands each morning to defecate at the edge of the road just a few metres from her house.

It was clear that her family, and many others, simply do not have the money to build a 20,000-rupee or 25,000-rupee latrine. As Sohni Devi pointed out in Chapter 4, if they did, they might instead choose to use the money to build a room for their house. Still, there are others who could afford to spend that much money but chose not to build a latrine for their most vulnerable members. Many more could afford an internationally normal pit latrine for one-tenth this price. To be sure, this problem is not unique to rural India: In households and in policymaking, people in many countries are less than generous when it comes to the needs of the old and disabled.

Economists characteristically recommend public policies that cause a Pareto improvement – meaning policies that make some people better off without making anyone worse off – even if they increase inequality. But to apply this idea successfully, you must be very sure that, say, a rich person becoming richer does not make the poor worse off. For example, one way that economists typically think the poor might be made worse off by the rich getting richer, even if there is no change in their own wealth, is if increased inequality in society undermines democratic accountability for everyone.

When a rich villager acquires a fancy latrine with a huge pit, it would seem to be a Pareto improvement: The rich person is better off and poorer villagers are the same as before, except the whole village is exposed to less of somebody's faeces. However, if such a change teaches the poor households in the village that internationally normal latrines are socially unacceptable (why else would the rich neighbour pay for this, after all?), the old or disabled who might otherwise benefit from a simple latrine are plausibly made worse off. By seeking to avoid emptying of pits and ritual pollution, rich, often higher-caste, people build expensive latrines and therefore reinforce the definition of what a usable latrine is for the rest of the village.

A wealthy middle-caste man in Gujarat who owns two latrines with large pits explained to us that he does not expect his poorer neighbours, who belong to a marginalized Adivasi group, to build latrines, or even to use the latrines they receive from the government. 'The [latrines] that you get from the government are no use, they are so small ... their pits are so small that they fill up in two or three months. There will be bad smells and filth in the surroundings. For Adivasi people, who don't have much land, wouldn't they make a house rather than a latrine? [If they made latrines] it would be dirty,' he said.

We did meet a handful of families who had built affordable latrines for elderly or disabled relatives. But the ways in which they talked about their latrines, or avoided doing so, ultimately confirmed that such latrines are widely understood to be socially unacceptable. Diane met one family who had an adult son who was crippled by polio and could not walk. They were so embarrassed to own a rudimentary latrine that, even after they had spent an hour completing the SQUAT survey, the family would still not admit that the pit and slab by the side of their house – clearly used for defecation – was actually a latrine. Another elderly man admitted that he owned a latrine, but declined to show it to us. His grandson later pulled Diane aside and explained that his grandfather was embarrassed that it was so simple and inexpensive. It was a perfectly normal pit latrine by WHO standards.

Who wants a subsidized latrine?

Why would a government want to give its rural citizens latrines? We have seen several reasons: because one family's open defecation kills and stunts another family's children, because disease in early life reduces the productivity of workers throughout the economy and because there is a minority of rural Indians who suffer indignity without one. Although these reasons overlap, they suggest different policies: to promote health you must promote latrine use among the majority; to promote dignity you need merely to supply a latrine to the minority of people who already want one. Designing the right policy requires asking: Who would readily want to use a latrine if the government gave them one?

To many observers outside of India's villages, *women's* dignity is a reason for the public provision of subsidized latrines. People take it as obvious that women in rural India suffer from being required to defecate in the open. We have seen that this is not necessarily true, and that the fact that women are more likely to use available latrines than men are may be because their families do not approve of them leaving the house either for defecation or for other purposes. However, there is an important link between latrine ownership and dignity for the old and the disabled, for whom defecating in the open is difficult.

Moreover, these are not the only rural Indians who might appreciate a subsidized latrine: According to the IHDS, about one in ten rural Indians are Muslim. The SQUAT survey showed that people in Hindu households are much less likely to use a government latrine than one that they buy or make for themselves, but there is no similar gap for Muslim households. Muslims are equally likely to use both publicly and privately constructed latrines.

All of this suggests that there exists a minority of rural Indians who would like to use a subsidized latrine, although perhaps not the particular minority that urban journalists and policymakers assume. It is reasonable to wonder whether a *targeted* scheme of public latrine construction could give latrines to people who are likely to use them, without wasting resources on those who are not.

Yet, targeting itself is difficult and distortionary, and the local politicians and contractors who earn money from each latrine are unlikely to be much help in identifying the households to leave out. More importantly, if there are only so many political, financial and human resources available for rural sanitation policy, such a targeted construction scheme would likely consume all the attention that might otherwise be available for making a larger change in the majority's open defecation behaviour. The best policy response to this trade-off is a question on which well-intentioned people could disagree, even informed by the surprising facts of open defecation. The policy response that rural India actually receives, and the prospects for and constraints on a better policy, are the topics for the final part of this book.

Responses

8 | Policy: Politics, development and latrine construction

The Government of India maintains a website which makes precise statistical claims about rural sanitation. Users can click through states, districts, blocks and years to read exactly how many latrines the government has paid for in each patch of rural India. Such detail irresistibly invites a sanitation researcher to visit the handful of the villages where the computer system recorded the best performance. So, in Sitapur, during the summer monsoon of 2012, Dean and his friend Avinash did.

These villages indeed did have more latrines than the average village in Sitapur. Still, open defecation remained visibly commonplace. Each of the statistical superstars disappointed with a unique variation. In one, the village leader enthusiastically recalled the sanitation award he had received for his accomplishments. He sent a boy to fetch the trophy for a photo. He explained that he had received the trophy for excellence in speedy latrine *construction* – evidently unaware that we (and those who gave the award) were hoping that his village had achieved latrine *use*.

When we arrived at another village, the pradhan was sitting at a small desk outside the house of the village secretary, a

173

bureaucrat appointed by the Uttar Pradesh government to oversee development projects. By our fantastic luck, they were puzzling over how to complete a one-page village survey form that was intended to be the baseline assessment of the Nirmal Bharat Abhiyan, a short-lived, then new sanitation programme.

They were caught in a dilemma: They could not decide whether they should claim that everybody in their village indeed has the latrines that they received funding for under the last sanitation programme or whether they should admit that everyone still defecates in the open, seizing the opportunity to get their hands on a new round of construction funds.

The leaders of a third village skipped straight to the point. As Avinash and Dean were interviewing the pradhan, one of his male relatives spotted us and asked with unconcealed delight: 'Are we going to receive some *vikas*?' The Hindi word he used typically translates to 'development', but in his family and throughout the *vikas* business, everybody understood the word's real meaning: funds for government construction projects that can be redirected to local politicians and bureaucrats in the process.

The last two chapters of this book are about policy responses to the challenges we have seen: programmes and plans of the Indian state and international development agencies that are intended to speed the reduction of open defecation. In Chapter 2, when we first encountered the mystery of open defecation in rural India, we eliminated a series of non-explanations, including governance. Governance, we wrote, has not been a solution to open defecation in rural India, but nor is it to blame. We reiterate this here: Many countries with worse governance than India have much less rural open defecation. Within India, variation in rural sanitation does not track variation in governance quality across Indian states. This is likely because – as important as governments are to large sewer and waste treatment projects, especially in cities – evidence from other developing countries shows that the transition in behaviour from rural open defecation to rural latrine use has been largely undertaken by individual households for their own reasons.

Yet, India's rural sanitation policy deserves a close look. It receives considerable attention and resources; it possesses unrealized opportunities to do important good; and we suspect the challenges facing sanitation policy are similar enough to other development issues that a better understanding of them could be broadly useful. As before, our attention is drawn to puzzles. The puzzles in this chapter are *descriptive*: they are about why sanitation policies and programmes are as they are. The puzzles we explore in the next and final chapter are *prescriptive*: they are about what sanitation policy should try to do in rural India.

This chapter is about understanding rural sanitation policy as it exists and is practised. It is based on the same materials as the chapters before: statistics, official reports and interviews and events that we have experienced. In this chapter, we ask two questions. First, we ask why the Indian state does what it does. Why does the Indian state build so many unused latrines, perpetuating (under a series of labels) one basic programme design, rooted in construction, that essentially every rural sanitation expert agrees has not worked? Why does it publish such detailed online records claiming to describe latrine construction in every corner of rural India, despite widespread agreement that the data is substantially incorrect? Why do these activities receive endorsement and some funding from large international development agencies?

We also ask a second, more difficult-to-answer question: Why is sanitation policy in rural India not better designed around its challenges, despite the lessons of evidence and experience? Why is there no well-funded or well-staffed effort to promote latrine use and behaviour change? Why is there no credible public survey tracking open defecation – rather than reporting latrine construction – and monitoring and managing progress towards the 2019 goal? Why do the documents and employees of neither the Indian state nor the international development agencies emphasize the central challenges of caste? Are these possible activities absent because of high costs or low benefits? Are they too difficult, or too undesirable, and in either case to whom?

The simplest explanation for why the government enacts the policies it does is because its leaders believe they make good policy sense. Of course, trying to free Indian children from the disease spread by open defecation certainly would make good policy sense. Sanitation is the sort of task that governments are needed for. But we have seen that the enduring tactic of state latrine construction does little to reduce open defecation in India. So, if the government believes this plan makes good policy sense, we would also have to explain why the government is lastingly mistaken and why it does not invest in learning from its mistakes. Such an optimistic theory cannot resolve this chapter's puzzles: For example, measuring open defecation also would make good policy sense; measurement is essential to any effort to manage its decline; and a useful survey would be too inexpensive not to do. But such a survey is not done. So, to understand policy as social scientists, eventually this chapter will need to ask about politics.

Swachh Bharat Mission: A lot more of the same

On 15 August 2014, India's first Independence Day under Prime Minister Modi, the premier set a precise, quantitative goal: India would fully eliminate open defecation by 2 October 2019, the 150th anniversary of Mohandas Gandhi's birth. Suddenly, sanitation had the recognition of a personal project of the prime minister. The logo of the Swachh Bharat Mission (SBM) – Gandhi's round glasses – appeared throughout India's capital cities, in government offices, petrol stations, shopping malls and airports.

In 2014, we were optimistic that the SBM would be a serious effort to accelerate the decline of open defecation in rural India. Instead, it has replicated what has come before: the previous government's Nirmal Bharat Abhiyan, and the Total Sanitation Campaign and the Central Rural Sanitation Programme before that. The main difference was that the scale of the new programme was supposedly much, much bigger: The prime minister promised that the SBM would quickly provide a latrine for each of the 12.3 crore households without one. Yet even after, and perhaps even *because of*, the SBM's ambitious latrine construction targets, the government has not articulated a feasible plan to achieve it.

The prime minister committed to reduce open defecation from approximately half of the population (and over 70 per cent of the rural population) to zero, within five years. Figure 9 depicts the challenge. This graph uses Demographic and Household Survey data to show that the decline in open defecation in India has been slow. Although data is scarce, the pace is seemingly uninfluenced by alternations of political power in the 1990s and the next decade. If anything, the graph overstates the speed of decline in open defecation because it uses household-level data which ignores the fact that households that defecate in the open have, on average, more people in them than those that do not.

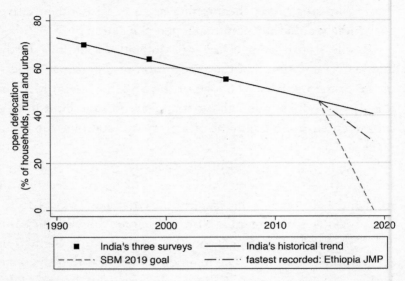

Figure 9. Eliminating open defecation by 2019 would have required an unprecedented acceleration in 2014

To achieve the 2019 goal, the pace of decline of open defecation in India would have to have already accelerated by more than a multiple of twelve. Quantitatively, such an accomplishment would be unprecedented. According to the Joint Monitoring Programme of UNICEF and the WHO – the world's official record keeper on sanitation statistics – no country has ever come close to a decline in open defecation by 50 percentage points over a period of five years.

According to the UNICEF–WHO Joint Monitoring Programme's estimates, Ethiopia has the record, with a decline by about 17 percentage points over five years in the 2000s. At the time, its population was about 6 per cent as large as India's.

This winning speed is less than one-third of the pace that all of India would have had to maintain during the SBM to meet a 2019 goal. Less encouraging still is that sanitation experts have questioned the accuracy of the Ethiopian data. If the Ethiopian data does in fact overestimate that country's decline in open defecation, Laos would hold the record with a decline of about 14 percentage points over five years. But it would be hard to draw lessons for India – a country of 1.3 billion people – from a country whose population is smaller than many Indian districts. Further, even when open defecation in these two countries was falling quickly, neither of them came particularly close to completely *eliminating* open defecation, which may be the hardest part.

One question we unfortunately will not be able to answer in this chapter is why the 2019 goal appeared: Why did sanitation get the brief attention that it did in 2014, when the prime minister committed the government to this ambitious goal? We do not know. But, this review of the historical record suggests that even if the government were willing to put more effort and money behind rural sanitation than any previous government, eliminating open defecation by 2019 would still be extremely ambitious. The 2019 goal may even have established a perverse incentive for bad public management: Any sort of realistic planning to accelerate the end of open defecation at an achievable pace must imply that there will still be open defecation in 2019.

Later in this chapter, we will look at the small piece of the Swachh Bharat Mission – 3 per cent of the total budget – that is supposed to be dedicated to changing defecation behaviour. Here, though, we consider the government's spending on latrine construction. We do this not because we wish to suggest that the government should start by spending more to build latrines that most people do not want, but because if we want to learn about the Indian state, it makes sense for us to start by looking at what it does.

In speeches and in the newspaper, the prime minister promised that the government would build a toilet for every household. Because over 12.3 crore households reported lacking a toilet or latrine in the 2011 census, this amounted to promising to build about 67,000 new latrines per day over a five year period. Reporters quickly noticed that there are 86,400 seconds in a day.

Under the SBM, each latrine is supposed to be subsidized at 12,000 rupees, which is far more than the cost of good, pit latrines in other developing countries. So ignoring all administrative and transaction costs, this adds up to a promise to spend 150,000 crore rupees – or 30,000 crore rupees per year over five years – on constructing expensive rural latrines. These dazzlingly large numbers give the SBM an important appearance and obscure the extent to which it represents a continuation of what came before.

How much is the government actually allocating to the SBM? Is the actual allocation a large fraction of the amount it would cost to build all of the latrines that have been promised? Accountability Initiative, a Delhi-based research group that tracks government budgets, found that the Central government in Delhi allocated to the Swachh Bharat Mission–Gramin (that is, the rural arm of the SBM) 2,850 crore rupees in 2014–15 and 8,915 crore rupees in 2015–16. These figures include the allocation of the Union Budget as well as money collected under the Swachh Bharat Cess – a special tax to help fund the SBM – and disbursed through a fund called the Rashtriya Swachhata Kosh.

These allocation figures are simultaneously large and small. They are large because the 2014–16 SBM allocation was about two and a half times what was allocated for rural sanitation during 2012–14. The government increased its funding for rural latrine-construction at a time when other social sector programmes were being cut. Further, Accountability Initiative found that most states indeed spent all of the money that had been allocated for SBM–Gramin, which is uncommon for rural development schemes. However, these figures are small compared to the over 30,000 crore rupees per year that the government would have to spend if it were actually going to build, in five years, a latrine for every household that lacks one – assuming every rupee went undiluted to construction.

Of course, it is little surprise that the government is underfunding latrine construction relative to what would be needed to meet its goal of building an expensive toilet for every household – governments everywhere often announce grand plans and end up spending only a fraction of what would be needed to achieve them. If there is a surprise, it is that such large-scale underfunding occurs in the context of the government openly encouraging the public to hold it accountable to a precise but unattainable quantitative goal, without itself tracking its progress towards the goal.

Seeming like a state

In the design and the implementation of the SBM, the Indian state omits to take ordinary, feasible steps of governance, widely recognized in political science as the core of what states do. One of these steps that states take is to document and officially interpret society – especially through statistics, a word that in its origins meant 'state affairs'. According to political scientist James Scott, 'The functionary of any large organization "sees" the human activity that is of interest to him largely through the simplified approximations of documents and statistics.' *Seeing Like a State*, Scott's 1998 book, is not about India in particular. Still, his thesis is alive in the string-tied stacks of papers and folders that fill district and block offices – signs of the weak grip of the Indian state on rural society. Scott explains that states need statistics and abstract summaries in order to do their jobs. State capacity is built by developing maps, statistics or other simplifications of society.

Scott wrote his book to warn about the cases in which states take this process too far. Sometimes, Scott realizes, rulers see a more convenient option than building a bureaucracy that can accurately summarize people's messy lives. Sometimes, it is easier for the state to rearrange people's lives to match a neat summary that fits in a file folder. Scott describes cases where states have relocated people to live in planned cities that look nicely square on maps, but destroy the commerce and sociality that make cities liveable. Some states have a history of wreaking even worse havoc while trying to order a manageable society.

Scott's point is that states so badly need data and a simplified understanding of society, that civil liberties can be overlooked and terrible things can happen to the people whose lives need to be rearranged to fit the state's purposes. The rural Indian state may initially resemble Scott's thesis: It would be hard to deny that state capacity in rural India is limited by the inability of bureaucrats to keep accurate statistics. Recall, for example, the pradhan and the secretary who were trying to decide how many latrines they could most profitably report needing on the Nirmal Bharat Abhiyan baseline 'survey'.

But a closer look suggests that rural sanitation policy is a case that may be at odds with Scott's thesis: The government appears to freely choose not to know what is going on. If Scott is worried that a ruler seeking power will scar his society in an attempt to write upon it, his analysis may overlook an opposite possibility suggested by sanitation policy in rural India: The state may look away. Scott tells us that official statistics can serve a political purpose when the state chooses to produce them; the case of open defecation in rural India suggests that official statistics can also serve a purpose when the state chooses not to.

The data that is not collected

In 2014, the prime minister announced plans for India to eliminate open defecation by 2019. But nobody knows what fraction of people in India defecated in the open in 2014, 2015 or 2016. And there is no serious plan of which we are aware to track this information going forward.*

It would be straightforward and inexpensive for the Swachh Bharat Mission to conduct or commission a survey to learn what fraction of people in rural India defecate in the open. A more useful (still inexpensive) survey could produce separate estimates for each of the states where most of the open defecation takes place, tracking change over time every year or every other year. Instead, the guidelines of the SBM outline a goal to rapidly eliminate open defecation from India – three times as fast as the next fastest decline in recorded history – without monitoring this simple statistic.

We know that a survey to measure open defecation in rural India is inexpensive and feasible because we have done one. The SQUAT survey produced informative estimates for well under five million rupees. But even a tracking survey that cost

---

* An update written during the final revision of this book in January 2017 is on page 260 of Notes.

fifty million rupees each year would amount to a tiny fraction of 1 per cent of the cost of building 1.23 million latrines over five years at 12,000 rupees apiece.

If commissioning a new survey is nevertheless too costly, questions about latrine use could be incorporated into the excellent national surveys that the Government of India already conducts. The National Sample Survey Organization has recently asked about latrine use in its large sample surveys, but has not done so in the person-specific, balanced way that produces credible estimates; this could easily be changed. If even this is too difficult, the government could allow the Demographic and Health Surveys to collect this information. These surveys are routinely collected in other countries throughout the developing world to track important demographic statistics such as infant mortality rates and child height. It would be straightforward to include among the India-specific modifications of the survey form a person-by-person question on latrine use.

Yet, successive Central governments have been slow to permit the collection of Demographic and Health Survey data. The Indian government last permitted a completed Demographic and Health Survey in 2005–06. In the decade since then, Bangladesh has released three such surveys, while Afghanistan, Cambodia, the Democratic Republic of the Congo, Kenya, Nepal, Sierra Leone and many other countries have released two each.

The paradox is that states are supposed to *want* statistical data: Scott famously worries that states will take this desire too far in the attempt to expand their power. Quantitative summaries allow states to govern, and they project an impression of control. Even if a ruler does not personally care what the maternal mortality rate is, it legitimizes his regime that he produces an estimate of one. So, if a state chooses not to collect what is elsewhere standard data worldwide, perhaps there is a good reason.

A recent example is the ongoing, multi-year census of Afghanistan. The only prior national census was conducted in 1979. Since then, no data has reported exactly how many people there are in Afghanistan. Exactly as Scott might predict, the census is now attempting to standardize Afghan names and requires that respondents report a surname. The census also asks whether households have a toilet. But the Afghan census does not ask which ethnic group respondents belong to. Therefore, nobody knows exactly how many Pashtuns and how many Tajiks there are in Afghanistan. Attempting to produce these figures would only invoke the politics of ethnicity, and would give politicians and others a reason to reject the whole exercise. It serves the state's purposes better not to know.

One might not imagine that ethnic conflict in Afghanistan and open defecation in India would be in the same category of political unknowability. But the SBM has announced an unrealistically ambitious goal, and the world expects India to be doing something about its open defecation. This presents a dilemma: The state can neither achieve success nor document failure.

Yet, having no data whatsoever could be as bad as admitting that the state is not attempting to significantly change rural open defecation. So, what is needed is statistics of a different sort.

The data that we do have

Recent technologies have reduced the (already modest) cost of collecting sample survey data. Surveyors can now record answers on tablet computers, instead of on paper forms that must be entered into a computer by another person. But collecting survey data still requires hiring, training and supervising surveyors who must visit villages, interact respectfully with respondents and collect answers to questions. A surveyor must look at something, measure something or ask someone a question. The hard part is making sure this person has an incentive to do his job well and truthfully. The human and transportation costs are approximately the same as they were a few years ago before smart tablets.

In contrast, recent technology has considerably reduced the cost of *appearing* to have a vast depth of statistical data. It is easy to develop a complex statistical website that lets readers click through numbers into further tables, transform columns of figures into coloured graphs and 'dive deep' into finer disaggregation. It is again easy to have a flexible database behind the website, so that its managers can periodically enter updates. With so many bells and whistles, many readers will never wonder whether the abundant data contains reliable information.

The highly modern Ministry of Drinking Water and Sanitation website does not attempt to show how many people defecate in the open. Nobody is counting latrine use. Instead, the website records the number of toilets for which funds have been spent.. The figures can be aggregated by village, block, district or state and are available for each year. This has been true for the SBM and for the two central sanitation programmes before it, which had essentially similar statistical websites.

The website appears dazzling in its quantitative precision, yet the data never involves a source of information from outside the state and its immediate agents. Each aggregated data point reflects administrative records entered by a government employee. In the district offices we have visited most often, latrine completion figures are entered by a tiny staff of one (maybe two) data entry operators using one (maybe two) computers. In many cases, no regular government employee has the computer skills for the task, so the data is entered by consultants, motivated by eleven-month contracts. These few contractors struggle to enter piles of paper records submitted by block officials.

There are no independent observers responsible only for collecting accurate facts. If the district data entry operator, in principle, ever wanted to visit a village to double-check the data on paper forms, he would have to seek approval from a senior official to be away from the office and use the official car for something absurd that is not in his job description. Assuming that, within one day, the computer operator could indeed learn accurate information about sanitation in a village, at that rate it would take three years to complete a district. Yet, even this scenario is fantastically unrealistic; lower-ranking bureaucrats and consultants have little incentive to report the truth – they are incentivized to complete their jobs, as measured by whether forms are filled.

The tugboat of state

Much is unique about open defecation in rural India. But one aspect may be surprisingly similar to other parts of the developing world: the limited role of the state in promoting the widespread switch from open defecation to the use of basic latrines. In this section, we present the hypothesis that the power of the Indian state over rural open defecation is limited, in part because the state lacks the human resources needed for behaviour change, and in part because the social forces against it are strong. If correct, this would partially reflect the special challenge of sanitation – where the construction projects in which the rural state specializes are insufficient at best and distracting at worst – but we would expect similar difficulties if the state attempted other changes in behaviour within households in rural India.

This may sound absurd if you have read this far. Throughout this book, we have emphasized sanitation as a classic public good, perhaps the clearest example of what collective action and government should be for. But the best examples of state promotion of sanitation are urban infrastructure, not rural behaviour change. This is no argument that the state should not attempt to change rural sanitation behaviour when and where it can. Rather, our point is that we should not conflate the challenges of promoting rural latrine use with the unambiguous historical record of states helpfully investing in pipes, clean water and sanitary sewerage systems. There is no contradiction between the possibilities that, on the one hand, households outside of India have typically switched from open defecation to latrine use for their own reasons and, on the other hand, states have managed the further transition to piped sewers, especially in cities.

We suspect that this conjecture would also sound absurd to many of our colleagues working in international development: They experience first-hand the money spent, the conferences held and the documents produced about each step in the succession of policies – and their own hard work. From this vantage point, the state appears active, not limited, with programmes everywhere, meetings about everything and written guidelines for every goal. However, the policymaking activity that accompanies an outcome is not sufficient to conclude that the activity caused the outcome. It is increasingly widely recognized how difficult it is to be confident about cause and effect for big policies and programmes, especially in a world where poverty and health are both improving rapidly almost everywhere.

———⁓———

So, what about rural open defecation? Has its reduction typically resulted from state action? In Chapter 4, we saw that the latrine pits that get used in rural India tend to be built or funded privately by their owners and made with very large pits or tanks. Although sanitation in rural India differs in many ways from the rest of the world, the practical importance of private latrine construction may be an important point in common. The difference, of course, is that such private investment has happened more often elsewhere than in India.

In 1995, Marion Jenkins and Val Curtis conducted qualitative interviews in rural Benin to ask why some people wanted latrines at a time when few did. They found that households were not motivated by the public good or by their neighbours' health. The few who built a latrine did it for the prestige: 'Status conferred by latrine ownership comes from their symbolic ability to display an owner's affiliation with the urban world, to express modern views about home comfort and new values related to time and money gained outside the village and to emulate some of the privilege, wealth and status of old royalty.' Jan Willem Rosenboom and co-authors found something similar in rural Cambodia: 'Household decisions seemed to be more driven by status, convenience and other lifestyle benefits resulting from latrine ownership than by considerations of better health.' They describe a context where it was the role of the government to 'support the marketing and sales of latrines to households and, on occasion, act as commissioned sales agents', but nobody expected that it was the job of the state to give everyone a latrine.

When we hear sanitation policy professionals advocating the promise of a government-led approach to rural sanitation, they are often recommending an approach based on Community-Led Total Sanitation, or as it is abbreviated, CLTS. Such conversations almost always invoke the CLTS movement in Bangladesh – where open defecation is now rare, and where CLTS was first widely implemented, although not originally by the Bangladesh government. For example, one World Bank policy brief summarizes: 'Over the last decade, Bangladesh has emerged as a global reference point in experimenting with and implementing innovative approaches to rural sanitation. The Community-Led Total Sanitation (CLTS) approach was one such innovation that helped to move over 90 million people from open-defecation towards fixed-point defecation.'

The CLTS movement holds that villages can become 100 per cent open-defecation-free if social forces are used to invoke people's disgust at open defecation and to encourage them to change together. Under CLTS, those who resist switching away from open defecation are to be shamed into compliance by their neighbours. Public subsides of latrines, in this view, are not only unnecessary; they are harmful because they change how the household views the latrine. Ironically, we now often hear enthusiastic reports from countries where community-led sanitation has become government-led.

Was CLTS responsible for Bangladesh's low population-level rates of open defecation? Or did both happen in the same place without one causing the other? We can use the sort of survey data that is unfortunately absent in India to think about this question in Bangladesh, where there have been six Demographic and Health Surveys (DHS). The first was in 1994; the most recent was in 2011. Open defecation in these surveys is plotted in Figure 10 – each point is a DHS survey round – alongside the results of the three DHS surveys conducted in India. Three of Bangladesh's surveys were conducted before CLTS was invented in 2000 and three were conducted afterwards. The trend suggests that open defecation declined at a steady rate over this period. There is no evidence of any speeding or slowing of the rate of decline in open defecation after CLTS was introduced.

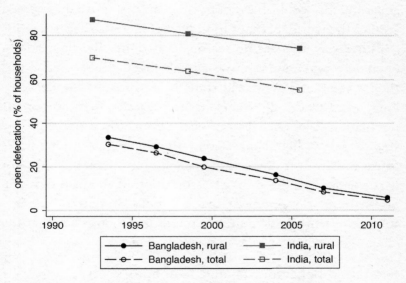

Figure 10. The long, steady decline of open defecation in Bangladesh

Perhaps in Bangladesh too the average household moved on from open defecation for its own reasons. Of course, this constant decline does not definitively prove that CLTS did not help. For example, we cannot rule out that CLTS made it easier to reach the last remaining stragglers. Even if CLTS did speed the decline of open defecation, that would not imply that what works in Bangladesh necessarily offers the correct prescription for India. As we have seen, cultural differences between predominantly Muslim Bangladesh and largely Hindu India are good reasons to doubt that sanitation recipes are portable to India.

As researchers hoping to contribute to better lives for the poor, we often worry about an uncomfortable truth: It is not easy to trace the effect of ideas on policy. Has CLTS importantly changed population-level sanitation behaviour? Or has it merely offered an attractive label for what some resource-poor governments would have done anyway? As CLTS has spread around the world, perhaps both have sometimes happened.

Either way, there is no reason to attribute the Bangladeshi open defecation rate that was already low in 1994 to what was then a weak and contested state. More broadly, the decades-long experience of Bangladesh suggests that important population-level changes can occur even in a context of low state capacity: Big changes sometimes happen without states causing them. Of course, this conclusion seems obvious, but it stands against the implicit assumption of much rhetoric in international development that attributes important changes to governments by default. It reminds us to look closely at the chains linking big policies to people's lives.

Sanitation behaviour change is nobody's job

Earlier in the chapter, we wrote at length about the funds allocated by the SBM for building standardized government latrines. We wish that there were as much information available to write about an active campaign for behaviour change, working to change people's minds and encourage them to switch to latrine use. Although we would be delighted to learn of a low-cost programme, such as through mass media, that causes people to use latrines, we suspect that the persuasion required would be highly labour-intensive: village to village, perhaps face-to-face.

For this reason, when the SBM guidelines were being prepared in October 2014, our colleagues Aashish Gupta and Payal Hathi called for an 'army' to implement the Swachh Bharat Mission. They wrote in the *Indian Express*: 'What we need is a sanitation *sena* – an army of frontline workers, one in every village, responsible solely for motivating and sustaining latrine use.'

Two months later, this language found expression in the guidelines, attached to jobs that, on paper, already existed: 'An army of "foot soldiers" or "swachhata doots" on sanitation could be developed and activated.' The guidelines continue:

> These would be through using existing arrangements like panchayati raj institutions, cooperatives, ASHAs, anganwadi workers, women groups, community-based organizations, self-help groups, water linemen/pump operator etc., who are already working in the GPs [gram panchayat] or through swachhata doots, engaged specifically for the purpose. In case existing employees of other line departments are to be utilized, their original line departments have to be in clear agreement to the expansion of their roles to include activities under the Swachh Bharat Mission.

Yet, existing health and community workers have little reason to take up the task of convincing people to use latrines when they will not be compensated for doing so. And despite the fact that sanitation experts agree that the government should put greater emphasis on behaviour change than latrine construction, the government has not allocated funds to hire a staff for this purpose. Behaviour change is nobody's job. It is no wonder, then, that the programme guidelines never precisely specify who will do this work. The language carefully avoids sentences with human subjects: 'emphasis is to be placed'; 'behavior change communication should focus'; 'delivery mechanisms would be adopted'.

Not only does the Swachh Bharat Mission, unlike other social programmes such as the Integrated Child Development Scheme or the National Rural Employment Guarantee Scheme, not provide for the much-needed staff; worse still, its guidelines limit the amount that can be spent on 'Information, Education and Communication (IEC)'. The guidelines specify that no more than 8 per cent of the overall budget can be spent on IEC. The amount that is in fact spent on behaviour change is even less than this: In 2016–17, Accountability Initiative found that only about 1 per cent of the Swachh Bharat Mission budget was spent on trying to convince people to use latrines.

The Indian state is small

It is no accident that this book has allocated three chapters to social forces and individual choices, but only one chapter to the state. In scholarly studies of Indian politics, the observation that India is 'all society, no state' is an old one. We revisit this adage here in part because sanitation is an important case for human welfare, where the absence of state leverage is particularly clear. Primarily, we feel compelled to cover this old ground because people in Delhi, on the news and at international conferences appear to believe the opposite – that there is nothing that the Indian state cannot control.

The World Bank produces figures for each country on 'Government Final Consumption Expenditure' (GFCE) as a percentage of GDP. This includes all government spending on goods and services, including payments to employees. Over the five years from 2010 to 2014, the average country spent 17 per cent of GDP on government. GFCE in the United

States is close to the global average, at 16 per cent. Sub-Saharan African and Latin American countries average 16 and 15 per cent, respectively. Sierra Leone and Sweden are both towards the top of the list, at 26 per cent, for different reasons. We suspect that many Indian observers would be surprised to learn that India – at only 11 per cent – is in the nineteenth percentile from the bottom.

We often hear policy experts in Delhi rhapsodize the power of district magistrates: these are early-career Indian Administrative Services (IAS) officers responsible for essentially all aspects of the administration of one of India's districts numbering over 600. International development professionals often hope to persuade a district magistrate to take decisive interest in their cause. Yet, one IAS officer we know recalls something other than a sense of unchecked power, back when he was a young district magistrate: Papers to sign piled up so quickly that he barely had time to find the correct spot to add his signature to each one. Reading them was out of the question.

The next time you hear about the magisterial power of an Indian district magistrate, substitute the title with the roughly demographically equivalent 'chief of state of a Central American or small sub-Saharan African country'. Better yet: 'unelected, immigrant chief of state of a Central American or small sub-Saharan African country, lacking almost all staff, and whose term is limited to about a year'. The average district in India is home to two million people. The districts in Uttar Pradesh that we know best are considerably larger. Many districts manage with approximately the same population size and infant mortality rate as Sierra Leone or Liberia, two African countries facing deep human development challenges. But Indian districts have no ministries of health, education, statistics or commerce, and are assisted by no well-staffed missions from the World Bank, the UN or international donors. It is neither any constraint unique to sanitation policy in particular nor the fault of the poor district magistrate if he (or, less frequently, she) is unable to govern a small country in the few months he lives there, even with the help of two data entry consultants and a driver.

In January 2015, there were 4,802 members of the elite Indian Administrative Service, or about one for every 260,000 Indian citizens. Of these, 1,379 are posted to the Central government. Four hundred eighty four are assigned to Uttar Pradesh – where one in eight humans who defecate in the open lives – which works out to one IAS officer for every 420,000 Uttar Pradeshis.

Of course, IAS officers are only a small fraction of the Indian state. India's Ministry of Statistics estimates that there are eighteen million formal public employees in India, of all kinds. In contrast, there are 5.7 million in the United Kingdom. Almost one in ten of the population of the UK is employed by the state in some capacity, compared with one in about every sixty-five persons in India. Expressing the human size of the state as a fraction of the size of the population is critical when the goal is not to build a waste-water treatment plant but rather to persuade 600 million citizens to change their sanitation behaviour. Open defecation will end one *capita* at a time.

Who wants a better rural sanitation policy?

Having surveyed what sanitation policy does and does not do, we are still left with a question: why? If these outcomes are the result of constraints, why is rural sanitation so difficult for policymakers and the state? Why is there no effective investment for overcoming these constraints? On the other hand, if these policy outcomes reflect not constraints but rather policy preferences, then whose? Who wants the SBM that rural Indians have?

When the government adopts a new policy or expands funding for an existing one, it makes sense to ask who is pushing for the change. For example, programmes that redistribute resources to the rural poor are often seen as an attempt to buy rural votes. In this case, many rural households will be receiving something from the SBM. Yet, rural voters cannot be the political interest group responsible for the SBM. As we have seen, rural Indians have little demand for the kind of latrines the government gives away. Nor do they have any demand for sanitation behaviour – change programmes: It is precisely rural voters' behaviour that must change if open defecation is to end. As useful as it would be, there is no reason to expect the large majority of rural Indians who defecate in the open to rise up at the polls and demand that the government figure out some way to make them stop.

What about other interest groups that seek to influence the state? What about national elites? Civil society? What about the so-called 'middle class' or the rural political elites? As we will see, in the case of rural sanitation, none of these politically important interests was asking for the government to put an end to rural open defecation. The problem of open defecation does not fit the standard political categories familiar to national elites on the right or on the left.

Debates about addressing open defecation in Indian popular media are almost always in the language of latrine construction. Open defecation in rural India is a difficult problem to solve merely by allocating money. The political right in India objects to what they characterize as wasteful entitlement programmes:

spending public funds to transfer private benefits to the poor. Some may see no reason to add latrine construction to the list. Prominent voices on the right emphasize that the government budget is a leaky bucket, that every tax is distortionary somehow, that there is always an opportunity cost of government spending and that there is a limit to what the government can do. All of this is true, to some degree or another.

Yet, as Chapter 6 documented, negative externalities imply that reducing open defecation is too good of an economic bargain for the standard fiscal argument to apply to this case. If building a latrine were all that were needed, the government would make a profit through increased wages and taxes even if it spent more per latrine than it proposes to do now. Yet, building a latrine is not enough. So, if only by coincidence, economic conservatives' standard argument has a point: Much of India's latrine construction may be a waste of money, if that is where the programme stops.

For entirely different reasons, national elites on the political left have not been the political interest group to advocate for changing sanitation behaviour either. When sanitation was a prominent policy issue in 2014, elites on the left called for the government to distribute free or highly subsidized latrines. To be clear, we certainly support the redistribution of a latrine's worth of value (or much more) to India's poorest households; but that support reflects our position on social welfare, not our research about effective sanitation policy. And, as we saw in Chapter 7, there are certainly many disabled and older people who would benefit from latrines but do not have the power within their households to cause them to be built. Targeting subsidized latrines to such people could be a good idea, if targeting itself were not so difficult.

For some on the left, the claim that public subsidy cannot solve an important problem would appear to challenge the very core of what the state is for: redistribution. What the political right objects to as 'entitlements', the left pushes for as 'rights'. But rights to receive government toilets are not a useful way to talk about a harm that citizens cause to one another. What Indian babies need is a right to be free from other citizens' open defecation behaviour.

For the reasons in Chapter 5, sanitation policy should be designed around the constraints on affordable latrine adoption imposed by caste, untouchability and social attitudes. Yet, people on the extreme cultural right have no objection to caste hierarchy and the remnants of untouchability, and people on the extreme economic left have no patience for such social details. The furthest left in India perceives a world of class conflict: Many reject Dalit struggles against caste hierarchy as a distraction from the ultimate goal of mobilizing a unified working class. So, they too are unlikely to set aside their core values for a nuanced, pragmatic position on sanitation. The battle between left and right never meets in the middle to evaluate the utilitarian, statistical evidence that open defecation causes externalities that have a surprisingly large effect on health and well-being.

If the elites will not advocate for better sanitation policy, what about the so-called 'middle class'? After all, the urban middle class is often conscious of India's international image, and high rates of open defecation increasingly tarnish that image. Yet, if India is 'islands of California in a sea of sub-Saharan Africa', as Jean Drèze and Amartya Sen have written, rural open defecation is entirely foreign to the urban middle class. The urban middle class does not defecate in the open.

Although their children too may be sometimes exposed to the open defecation of poorer neighbours, *rural* open defecation is a remote problem for them.

Moreover, there is little evidence that the urban middle class will champion a cause that may require changing how rural Indians think about caste and untouchability. Although some among the urban middle class oppose the caste hierarchy explored in prior chapters, many of them perpetuate it, albeit in different ways than villagers do. As we saw in Chapter 3, the India Human Development Survey asked respondents whether they practise untouchability. Fully 16 per cent of urban household respondents who classified themselves as Brahmin or forward caste admitted to the surveyor – a perfect stranger – that someone in their household practises untouchability. Education alone is unlikely to eliminate the problem: This fraction rises slightly to 18 per cent among urban Brahmin households where an adult has completed secondary school. To emphasize, this is not a subtle detection of implicitly biased behaviour. On the contrary, these respondents were prepared to confess *openly* to practising untouchability in a face-to-face survey.

To the extent that the urban middle class considers the problem of rural open defecation at all, the government may have convinced them that it is being solved. Soon after the prime minister issued a call for cleanliness in 2014, sanitation advertisements appeared in the kinds of stores and malls frequented by the urban middle class, signalling that the programme was off to an ambitious start. Now, in the third year of the five-year programme, among the few publicly remaining signs of the Swachh Bharat Mission are literal signs: boards and banners urging shoppers in upscale urban markets to adopt trash cans. One poster in the Defence Colony market in Delhi, titled 'Swachh Bharat Mission', encourages shoppers to 'clean up the clutter, shun the litter, make sure our markets glitter'.

So, if neither rural voters, nor national political elites on the left or right, nor the urban middle class can be expected to ask for better sanitation policies, this leaves rural political elites. Might rural local elites compel the state to address open defecation? One immediate reason to doubt this is that many village leaders share the views of their neighbours. They themselves often defecate in the open. Or, if they use a latrine, it has an enormous pit, sending a message to their neighbours that only expensive latrines are acceptable.

Rural elites matter to national politics in part because they organize and guide votes. They are two-way brokers: They influence the flow of resources from the state to the village, and they influence the flow of votes from their villages. It is well-known that rural construction projects are a particularly important currency in this brokerage. If so, rural political elites do have a substantial interest in a large, active rural sanitation programme. But the kind of programme they are interested in is not one that will convince people to build their own simple latrines, use them and empty the pit. Rather, they are interested in the kind of programme that we already have, one in which funds can be siphoned off from construction budgets and into their own pockets.

In Uttar Pradesh, most latrine funds are bundled with other government funds for building roads, electricity poles and other public buildings in the village. The name of this village development programme changes depending on which political party is in power. It is called the Dr Ambedkar Gram Vikas Yojana under Bahujan Samajwadi Party (BSP) governments and the Dr Ram Manohar Lohia Samagra Gram Vikas Yojana under Samajwadi Party (SP) governments – but the activities remain the same.

Recall Ramila, from Chapter 1. She received something that was not quite a latrine from the Government of Uttar Pradesh. Upon seeing the partially constructed latrines in Ramila's village, Diane decided to meet the village leader, Saif, to learn more about where they came from. Saif had applied for and been awarded the Dr Ambedkar Gram Vikas Yojana in 2011, near the end of Mayawati's fourth term as chief minister. He openly admitted to Diane that he had fudged the village population numbers on his application, claiming that the village had more Dalits than it did. Mayawati, who belongs to a Dalit caste, has strong political support among Dalits in Uttar Pradesh. It is widely believed that her party, the BSP, is more likely to choose a village with a large Dalit population.

Upon being awarded the Ambedkar Gram Vikas Yojana, Saif was disappointed to learn that he would only control funds for latrine construction: the money for the other parts of the programme would be handled by a contractor chosen by district officials. That limited his ability to extract money from the programme. However, with hundreds of households in the village, and a 4,500-rupee latrine subsidy per household, there was still plenty of money to be made if the latrines that he built did not actually have 4,500-rupee worth of parts.

In other settings, democratic pressure from villagers might have enforced that a first-term village politician provide latrines worth fully 4,500 rupees each, or at least close to it. Not in this case. Villagers did not want the latrines that the government was offering. So Saif faced no opposition from his voters when the masons and labourers he hired delivered little more than a few bricks cemented together and a few cement pit covers. What people did object to, however, was that Saif hired labourers from other villages to build the latrines, rather than spend the *vikas* to hire his own constituents.

When Diane asked Saif whether he had heard about the Nirmal Bharat Abhiyan's plan to increase the subsidy from 4,500 rupees per latrine to 10,000 rupees per latrine, his eyes widened. He started asking her questions. He realized, to his chagrin, that he had used his request for latrine funding at a time when the opportunity for corruption was only about half of what it would have been had his village been awarded latrines under the new Nirmal Bharat Abhiyan.

International development and its clients

A final group of people *does* often advocate for the Indian state to do something about open defecation: the agencies and institutions of international development. By 'international development' we mean the large, international organizations that fund and influence development policies and programmes around the world. International development, in fact, expects quite a lot out of developing states, holding them officially responsible for promoting almost every aspect of well-being. As we wrote the first draft of this chapter in 2015, the world was transitioning from the United Nations' Millennium Development Goals to the post-2015 Sustainable Development Goals. The original Millennium list was itself an ambitious set of quantitative targets; the new Sustainable list is even more detailed. Eight goals before 2015 have become seventeen, with 169 targets at last count. Included on the new list of what every country must do is to eliminate open defecation.

So, one possibility is that rural India's sanitation programmes happen in part because international development promotes, funds and expects them. If international development agencies have influence over sanitation policy, are they getting the sanitation programmes they want? Or could they push the Indian state towards effective behaviour change? Or is international development also constrained in its ability to address open defecation in rural India? If so, why?

One key constraint is that international development agencies have no uncontested source of political legitimacy outside of the governments with which they work, perhaps especially when these are democracies like India. So, it is not always clear how such agencies can – or if they should – usefully object when countries' policies appear wasteful, misguided or even harmful. It makes matters worse if a problem is localized, so familiar international solutions do not apply, or when culture is implicated, a topic that modern technocrats fear to touch.

Shanta Devarajan is the World Bank's chief economist for the Middle East and North Africa. Questions about the relationship between international development and governments are at the heart of his job. 'Poor people are poor because markets fail them, and governments fail them,' Devarajan writes on his blog. 'I think that most market failures, if they persist, are really government failures. The government does not find it in its political interest to correct them.' As Devarajan explains, this is not news: Economists have written about both market failures and government failures for a long time. Nor is it a surprise: 'The reason we see so many government failures is that decisions are taken by a chosen few.'

Devarajan, like almost everybody in such a high-ranking position in an international development organization, surely interacts often with government officials from developing countries. When Devarajan is meeting with these officials, he is thinking about poor children: 'Think how different it would be if a Minister of Health were accountable for child survival. We would see fewer high-end public hospitals in urban areas, better-functioning rural clinics with staff and medicines, and more spent on clean water and sanitation.'

Unfortunately, not everybody in international development agrees with Devarajan. One common answer to the dilemma of what international development should do in the face of governments that ignore the needs of their citizens is to define the dilemma away. The goal of international development becomes to support the projects of a country's government – whatever they may be. My own goal, many staffers reason, is to support the notions of the particular government bureaucrat with whom I am assigned to work. In this logic, Devarajan's dangerous category of 'government failure' is defined away – it cannot exist.

A business-like rhetoric enforces these ideas: The government is the 'client' of international development. This language appears in questions ('How will this reach our clients?'), in assertions ('Our new web-based tool is designed around our clients' needs.') and in everyday speech. The rhetoric of the consulting business serves an important function: It allows people to talk about the governments with which they interact without running the risk of accidentally talking about politics.

Deference to the client is an inversion of what many observers fear about international development agencies. In the 1990s, the World Bank and the International Monetary Fund were seen to offer to all developing countries a set of economic policy prescriptions known as the Washington Consensus. These market-oriented policies included low tax rates, trade liberalization, privatization of state industries and deregulation. By the early 2000s, the Washington Consensus had become an emblem of what many saw as wrong with international development: Uniform policies undifferentiated by country or population, to the apparent benefit of global economic elites. An anti-globalization movement emerged and raised some of the same good questions as anti-colonial movements before them: Who put rich countries in charge of the poor? Why should democratic governments, elected by poor people, not be allowed to govern themselves? Who is being served? Nancy Birdsall of the Center for Global Development expressed a widely shared view when, in 2009, she wrote of the World Bank and the IMF that 'in their current form – as Western-dominated trans-Atlantic clubs – these institutions lack legitimacy'.

Yet, imperfectly democratic domestic politics of developing countries can be as distant from the interests of the poor as were the plans of multinational corporations that became so infamous in the 1990s. This is especially true when a policy challenge is rooted in social inequality, such as this one.

Casting the government as the client of international development may seem apolitical: Development professionals are mere technocratic experts, consultants serving the national interests of the sovereign government. In the case of sanitation policy in India, this may entail helping to draft rules that describe ambitious projects with no staff to implement them, funding the district consultants that populate government websites with administrative statistics or repackaging those same statistics into visually compelling brochures with official logos. However, if these activities influence the public's perception of the goals and achievements of policy, this is a political choice in a world in which poor people are harmed by both market failures and by government failures. When international development agencies legitimize themselves by attaching themselves to government decisions, they help legitimize those decisions too.

Finally, social forces and cultural differences pose special challenges for international development. The first challenge is that they seem politically dangerous to organizations based in rich countries that are struggling to provide expertise without appearing colonialist. Tracing a problem to its social roots, even correctly, invites the criticism of prejudice. The second challenge is that identifying unique local causes of local problems may appear to undermine the need for global experts. If the attitudes that are perpetuating open defecation in India really are different from the attitudes that led to its decline in Bangladesh, it may not be obvious that international experts have any special advantage – unless, perhaps, they are the ones well trained and positioned to recognize international differences. In our own experience, colleagues and collaborators throughout the Indian state have typically found evidence for the role of casteism in rural open defecation to be persuasive, credible, perhaps even unsurprising; many in international development agencies have reacted as though we have committed an offensive transgression by bringing it up.

David Mosse is an anthropologist who, while studying and participating in development projects in rural India, famously turned his ethnographic gaze back at his development colleagues. Mosse spent the 1990s working with a British-government-funded development project among Bhil villagers in western India. As a researcher, he was hired to work with managers, implementers and villagers to construct an account of what was happening. Mosse realized that 'in the hugely complex cross-cultural world of development, most actors (including apparently powerful ones) have very little control over events. What is usually more urgent and more practical is control over the interpretation of events.' Project rules, he argued, were more nearly texts than manuals. Policy guidelines served symbolic purposes and were never intended as practical instructions. Like many academic 'evaluators', his expertise was brought in not to guide project choices but rather to provide an authoritative representation of whatever it was that happened anyway. Mosse wrote of an international development sector full of busy professionals, all collaborating to agree on a meaning of a world largely outside of their influence. Unsurprisingly, Mosse's book was not warmly received by the bureaucrats whose expertise he had interpreted as ritual.

Mosse is not the only observer to see the hectic world of policymaking as one engaged as much in interpretation as in control. Outside of development, the philosopher Dale Jamieson sees climate policy similarly. Jamieson suggests that any reduction in emissions, relative to what would have otherwise happened, has been altogether independent of international climate diplomacy: 'The undeniable fact is that the three main factors that have reduced [greenhouse gas] emissions are, in increasing importance: global recession, the collapse of communism and China's one child policy.' Not international climate policy. Instead, countries have more or less emitted what they see as in their long-run (or short-run) self-interest. Yet, climate diplomacy continues: 'Talking heads will talk, and all of this will seem very important to those whose job it is to track very important events, but will have little effect on anyone else or on the atmosphere.'

We hope Jamieson is too pessimistic about climate policy. We have organized our lives around the hope that Mosse's account of development policy is incomplete, that data and research can improve the lives of the poor by improving policy to effective ends. The evidence is overwhelming that some public projects, sometimes with the support of international development agencies, have indeed done much good – such as sanitary urban sewerage. Yet there is also clear evidence for two important, sobering facts: that the traction of the Indian state against important social forces such as caste is weaker than many development experts and professionals presume; and that, halfway through its schedule, the SBM is not producing useful, credible, feasible measures to track open defecation behaviour.

In the final chapter, we will turn from the sanitation policy that exists to the opportunities for a sanitation policy that could be. As a warning, we do not see any magic solutions. But, better sanitation policy is nevertheless worth working for – even a modest, partial acceleration of the decline of open defecation could prevent much suffering.

9 | Conclusion: The next rural sanitation policy

Years ago, when we first started discussing our research about open defecation in rural India, economists congratulated us on finding such a perfect policy issue for the application of economics. It was the model of a textbook negative externality with an easy policy solution: Poor people were being hurt by their neighbours' open defecation, so the government should start giving out free latrines. Subsidizing latrine construction would be one of the 'Pareto improvements' that economists search for: Everyone could be better off with no economic losers, because better health and greater productivity would more than compensate the people whose taxes bought toilets.

Eight chapters later, we have learnt that open defecation in rural India is far from this simple technocratic dream. Yes, open defecation is an important constraint on health and human capital – so much so that even imperfect improvements can have important benefits. Yes, the core of the challenge is external harm, economists' term for one person hurting another. Yes, there is every reason for the public sector to help lead the way towards a solution.

But many rural Indians have ideas that are not taken into account by the straightforward public economics of toilets. Open defecation in rural India is a challenge rooted in the social forces of caste and untouchability, which cannot be solved merely by distributing affordable latrines. And, as long as policy is shaped by politics, trying to persuade half of the population to change their behaviour may never become a priority.

This chapter is about what we have learnt from struggling to understand open defecation in rural India. First, it offers some final reflections on why open defecation is such an urgent problem for India. Then, it offers modest recommendations – what we would try, if we were put in charge of designing sanitation policy.

The challenges of open defecation raise many puzzles, but they make at least one thing clear. Even apparently technocratic problems can be more culturally, socially and politically complicated than they initially appear. This fact is old news to most development professionals and senior bureaucrats. It bears repeating because its prescriptions remain difficult to follow. Moreover, we think it may offer a special corollary in the era of the Great Escape: If governments and development agencies want to accelerate human development in places where the forces of the Great Escape are not working fast enough, these places may be the very situations where standard technocratic prescriptions are least likely to apply.

To be clear, such standard prescriptions are far from always wrong. The wide usefulness of the basic ideas of public health, economics and other enlightenment disciplines is why they are in the textbooks, after all. So, it is no surprise that experts jump to apply these proven solutions that have worked everywhere else to the cases where they are absent. But it may be that development efforts now and in the future can make the biggest extra difference – above and beyond the enormous improvements that are happening outside of policymakers' control – in the places where the Great Escape is encountering some special form of resistance.

Sanitation has a place at the foundation of the Great Escape. Its progress demonstrates the connections among the dimensions of well-being. As families get richer, sometimes they invest in latrines that they use; when they do, babies nearby have healthier childhoods and grow into healthier, more productive adults. As states get richer, sometimes they invest in sanitary sewer systems with similar consequences for early-life health, on a larger scale. Yet, in rural sanitation we can also see the inequality of the Great Escape. Children in India are shorter than children in Africa; children in West Bengal are shorter than equally poor children in Bangladesh; and babies born to Hindu households in India are more likely to die than babies born to Muslim households. Each of these inequalities can be hoped to eventually diminish as open defecation is eliminated everywhere; each reflects a difference in the pace of somebody's switching to latrine use.

The inequality of the Great Escape's progress presents a dilemma for development efforts. Policymakers have two defensible options. One option is to marginally speed up the already more rapidly changing places, accompanying success. For a government, this might entail focusing on those states or districts where most people are already rich enough to build large pits for themselves. For international development, examples of this might include working in countries where people already have and use imperfect pit latrines, and already want to buy something better. In such places, projects organize loans to stores that sell toilet parts, or otherwise smooth transaction costs for poor people who sometimes have trouble getting to the store or getting their cash together. These sorts of programmes offer a high probability of making people moderately better off, just like worthy public services in developed countries do. It is good work that somebody must do to ensure that the trains continue to run on time.

A more difficult option is to attempt to accelerate the lagging places like Uttar Pradesh and Bihar where open defecation remains normal and people see good reasons not to use an affordable pit latrine. The more ambitious path offers a greater possible reward, but also admits a greater risk of achieving nothing and wasting efforts and opportunities. The Millennium Development Goals of the first decade of the new millennium vowed to 'make poverty history'. That fits better on a T-shirt than 'possibly accelerate the existing slow decline of open defecation in rural India', especially if we take the space on the back of the shirt to explain that rural Indians will probably eventually make open defecation history anyway, if everybody waits long enough. But it matters enormously how long the wait would be. It is not too late to substantially reduce the harm that open defecation will cause before it runs its course.

India is running out of time to end open defecation

Open defecation in India will not be around forever. That is terrific news because children will be killed and stunted by open defecation as long as it continues in densely populated villages. But this terrific news has an ironic implication: It means that, if our goal is to save and improve lives, accelerating the decline of open defecation is urgent.

Imagine you were standing at the end of the twenty-first century, looking back at all the children who have been born in independent India's first 150 years. You would see that many of these children died at the very beginning of their lives.

Others survived childhood, only to be permanently scarred by infectious diseases that could have been prevented. If the children were rearranged by the year of their birth, you would see that the fraction killed and stunted due to open defecation declines over time – it is very high in the mid-twentieth century, gradually declining through the first decades of the twenty-first century and eventually falling to zero in the decades after this book is published. You would reach a point after which no more children would be killed by open defecation because open defecation had ended.

Now imagine that, informed by this perspective, it is your job to decide what to do about open defecation today, in 2017. Looking back in time, you see that most of the children who will ever be killed by open defecation are already dead; it is too late to save them. This is because open defecation has been declining and will continue to do so.

Looking forward, for the same reason, you can see that most of the remaining children who will be killed by open defecation will be killed in the *nearer* future, rather than further in the future. Because open defecation's costs are externalities (meaning, in this case, the health risk depends on how many of your neighbours defecate in the open) the extent of the bad consequences of open defecation in a particular year depends on how many people defecate in the open that year. Everything else being equal, open defecation will kill more children in a year when 40 per cent of Indians defecate in the open than in a year when 20 per cent of Indians do. Because open defecation is slowly declining over time, the year with 40 per cent open defecation will come before the year with 20 per cent open defecation does, so most of the deaths to come are coming soon.

If it were your job to decide what to do about open defecation and if you wanted to prevent child deaths, these facts would matter as you decide on a plan. Decision makers face important trade-offs which differ in the timing of action. For example, should development professionals incur the political costs of objecting to unrealistic sanitation policies or should they quietly lend their legitimacy to a bad idea in order to preserve their respectability and access, in the hopes of influencing the next government after an election in five years? Should we continue research until we are certain that we can scale up a strategy that works well, or should we get started with well-informed new strategies and make sure to learn systematically from trial and error as we go? Each of these choices can be reasonably defended, depending on the details of the situation.

We cannot know the true numbers, but if we assume that open defecation otherwise continues to decline linearly from 50 per cent at the rate of one percentage point per year, and if we assume that deaths due to open defecation are proportional to the fraction of people defecating in the open, about one-third of all future deaths due to open defecation in India will happen in the next ten years – that is, within only two short election cycles. In other words, if, hypothetically, policymakers could snap their fingers and eliminate open defecation but they waited ten years to do so, one-third of the achievable benefit would have evaporated. These deaths would have already happened.

Humanity's long transition from universal open defecation to universal safe disposal of faeces will be, we hope, a one-time event. The remaining years of this transition could pass quickly, or slowly, but when it is done nobody will be able to save or improve any more lives *by further* reducing open defecation. There will not be any more open defecation left.

–––~~–––

Economist Robert Gordon is worried that facts such as these mean that the rapid economic growth of the twentieth century will soon recede into the past. In Gordon's view, the Great Escape is really a one-time Great Transition: Life has been improving quickly because of a set of discrete switches spreading throughout the world, such as the adoption of safe sanitation or weatherproof houses with climate control. Of course, many people alive today do not have these improvements yet, but Gordon expects that in several more decades almost everyone will. Once everybody has made the switches (such as to toilet use), there is no reason to expect further large increases in living standards.

Gordon's view is not universally accepted among economists. Some economists who disagree suggest optimistically that standard quantifications of economic growth do not capture the continuing gradual improvements in well-being from technological progress. Skype accounts are one example that is obvious to us: They keep the two of us in touch across hemispheres, free of charge. Such improvements in people's lives may not be adequately reflected in economic statistics that follow the money.

However, money is not everything. Some of the most important indicators of the Great Escape are health and death. If limits to future economic growth remain debatable, limits to reducing human mortality and increasing human longevity are more clear. The evidence suggests that human populations can only be made to live so long. In fact, the vast majority of the increase in human life expectancy over the course of the Great Escape has been exactly the sort of one-time switch that Gordon writes about: from a pattern in which there are many infant and childhood deaths, including of the sort caused by open defecation, to a pattern in which almost everyone reaches adulthood and dies in old age. As demographer Eileen Crimmins has written, the implication is that one day, when almost everyone survives, it will be difficult to make further progress in the average length of human lives because increases in lifespan will have to come from causing older adults to die a little later.

Taking this long view shows us that we are in the middle years of a one-time demographic transition from nearly universal open defecation in rural India to its elimination; from infant death as a commonplace occurrence to nearly universal survival to old age. These facts mean that policymakers responsible for open defecation in India stand at a special moment in time, one that offers a short-lived opportunity. Speeding the decline of open defecation today is a chance to add to the total stock of human life and happiness in a way that will not be available to future policymakers, whose only option will be to struggle to help an aging population grow a little older.

Our best guess, based on the estimates in Chapter 5, is that around six million child deaths due to open defecation in India remain to occur in the future, and that about two million of these could be prevented by an acceleration that makes the decline proceed 50 per cent more quickly. These numbers are highly approximate, but they certainly illustrate that with the Great Escape churning in the background, there is no time to lose. If humanity misses this opportunity, we should not expect it to come back.

There is an important caveat to the fact that open defecation is slowly declining. Although the fraction of people in India who defecate in the open is declining, average *exposure* to open defecation increased between the 2001 and 2011 censuses by one important measure. Recall from Chapter 5 that the ill effects of open defecation depend on population density: Open defecation is particularly deadly in India because so many people live close together and close to one another's germs.

The decline in the *fraction* of Indians defecating in the open has been so slow that it was outpaced by *total* population growth between the 2001 and 2011 rounds of the Census of India. Over this period, the average person in India came to have more neighbours defecating in the open, not fewer. By this important indicator, the threat of open defecation is still going up.

The rate of population increase in India is declining, however. The United Nations World Population Prospects projects that population growth in India will fall below 1 per cent per year at some point between 2025 and 2030. Around this time, even if the fraction of Indians who defecate in the open continues to fall at the same slow rate, exposure to open defecation density will also begin to decline. (The details depend on how much population growth differs between those Indians who defecate in the open and those who do not.) Near 2070, the total size of the population of India is projected to begin decreasing. If the decline in open defecation accelerates, open defecation may end before then.

Another caveat is the worrying fact that the Great Escape is not guaranteed to continue. Rapid economic growth and declining mortality are recent trends amidst a long human experience of poverty and disease. These processes could stop. The politics of climate change, for an unfortunate example, show every sign of presenting a major challenge to future improvements in human well-being.

Another possible threat to the continued Great Escape is antimicrobial resistance. Open defecation contributes to this threat because it causes diseases which cause people to take antibiotics. Germs evolve to make humanity's antibiotic drugs ineffective – and this evolution happens more quickly the more often and the more carelessly antibiotics are used. Antibiotics are indeed used often and carelessly in India, as in other developing countries. When economists Jishnu Das and Jeff Hammer sent surveyor-patients to doctors in Delhi, they consistently found doctors prescribing antibiotics where they were not necessary – in many cases to meet the consumer demands of patients. Janet Currie, Wanchuan Lin and Juanjuan Meng found similar over prescription of antibiotics in China, where doctors receive financial incentives for the prescriptions. If these and other irresponsible uses of antibiotics (such as in agriculture) continue, antibiotic resistance could return us to the long era of infectious disease.

It is not immediately clear how best to respond to this threat. Antibiotics are sold in many tiny, privately owned shops and stalls throughout India, and they are undoubtedly instrumental in saving many lives. So, it would be difficult for a policy to separate good uses from bad, and enforce the distinction with the bluntness of a developing state.

Faced with this dilemma, one clear step would be to reduce the burden of disease, so that there is less demand for antibiotics. Ubiquitous open defecation in a setting of high population density and the easy availability of small packs of antibiotics may be the perfect ingredients for the resistant epidemic that experts fear. In India's 2005 Demographic and Health Survey, people who live in villages or urban blocks where more people defecate in the open take more medicine and pills, on average, after accounting for the fact that both toilets and medicine are more common in urban than rural India. This is despite the fact that medicine costs money, and poor people are more likely to defecate in the open. Most survey respondents did not know what medicine they were taking, but there is no doubt that many of these pills are antibiotics.

Unfortunately, acknowledging the threat of antimicrobial resistance, like serious discussions of India's other public health challenges, is politically sensitive in Delhi. A few years ago, Dean asked the public health office of a US state for data on antibiotic resistance that had been collected by hospitals and assembled by the state government. The office cheerfully provided it, with only the request to let them know if the research turned up anything useful for public health. At about the same time, Dean went to one of the leading teaching hospitals in India to make a similar request. Eventually, a researcher explained that such data is not collected. But if it were, it could not be shared with us. International collaboration on infectious disease research, Dean was told, had recently threatened the careers of other doctors in India. The government had reacted badly to news stories about antibiotic resistance, which is found all over the world, also being documented in a patient in Delhi.

State discouragement of scientific inquiry would be surprising if there were not cases of outright prevention of research on other topics. Unlike its neighbours, India has not had a Demographic and Health Survey in a decade. It does not attempt to estimate the fraction of persons who defecate in the open. The government recently shielded data on child stunting from the public until state-level summary statistics were leaked by the magazine the *Economist*. In India, public health data can be a political secret. If such is the response to antimicrobial resistance, preventing the need for drugs by reducing exposure to faecal germs may be all the more urgent.

A prediction: The SBM will not end open defecation by 2019

By the time this book is published in mid-2017, the five years of the Swachh Bharat Mission will be mostly over. So, it is not particularly bold to predict that open defecation will not be eliminated from rural India by 2019. Still, reflecting on current events in sanitation offers lessons for the next rural sanitation policy to come.

First, it is clear that the SBM, like sanitation programmes that have come before, is essentially a latrine-construction drive. When the non-partisan policy institute Accountability Initiative quantified progress towards the SBM in its 2016–17 Budget Brief, it found that latrine construction alone accounted for 97 per cent of the total expenditure between April 2015 and February 2016. Meagre spending on behaviour change as a fraction of the sanitation budget has *fallen* under the Mission, from 3 per cent of total expenditure in 2014–15 to only 1 per cent in 2015–16.

Second, there is little evidence that the SBM has reached the general public, and especially not with messages encouraging the use of affordable latrines. In the absence of a publicly available survey attempting to monitor the fraction of Indians who defecate in the open, Accountability Initiative conducted its own survey on the SBM. They surveyed villagers in ten districts, across five states. In only one out of the ten districts were more than 15 per cent of rural respondents aware of any type of sanitation promoter. In the median case, only 3 per cent of respondents were aware that someone from the government was encouraging, or supposed to be encouraging, people to use latrines. These results suggest a sanitation mission that is nearly absent from India's villages.

In collaboration with our colleagues at r.i.c.e., we have been conducting a phone survey. The survey applies the same techniques used by leading surveys such as the Gallup poll in order to produce a sample representative of adults in Delhi and a sample representative of adults in Uttar Pradesh. In late spring and early summer 2016, 2,708 people answered our questions. One question asked respondents whether they have heard of the SBM. With no probing or follow-up questions to weed out people who merely want to appear engaged, 62 per cent of people in Delhi claim to have heard of the SBM, similar to 63 per cent of urban Uttar Pradesh. The figure was 45 per cent in rural Uttar Pradesh.

To people who said they had heard of the SBM, we asked a harder question: What do you think the SBM does? We let people volunteer as many goals and activities as they could come up with, and categorized the responses. Most people thought the goal was general cleanliness, such as of houses and roads. This is an understandable answer, given the signs and ads that people see. Some people said that they thought the prime minister wanted them to clean up. Very few people included among their responses the idea that the SBM had anything to do with toilets or latrines: 5 per cent in Delhi, 6 per cent in urban UP, and only 4 per cent in rural UP. Among over 700 women interviewed in Uttar Pradesh, *not a single one* without education beyond secondary school mentioned that the SBM includes a goal about toilets or latrines. These results should come as little surprise: Both expenditure patterns and Accountability Initiative's survey results tell us that there is no meaningful effort to spread the word about open defecation in villages.

So, many people in India will almost surely still defecate in the open at the end of 2019. Is it unsporting to criticize the

SBM for failing to reach an unrealistic goal? Criticism is not our point. Instead, it is time to learn from this experience to make plans for what is next.

It is easy enough to say that a sanitation policy for rural India must focus on changing open defecation behaviour. Such a plan must find a way to address the reasons that rural Indians reject affordable latrines. But how, exactly? Unfortunately, we are not confident that anybody yet knows how to do this. We certainly do not. It would be nice if somebody could offer policymakers a ready and tested package of interventions, if all that were needed were the political rubber stamp: 'Proceed!' But no such package exists.

The revolution will not be computerized

These days, development professionals talk about 'what works' and tweet the latest quantitative evidence. The *New York Times* runs a blog called 'Fixes' that posts data-driven stories on social engineering problems such as traffic deaths in Delhi. The twentieth century may be looked back upon as an age of destructive technocratic excess, but in this century evidence-based managerialism is rapidly gaining Twitter followers. Indeed, in the view from Delhi, technocracy has merged the two meanings of 'technical': A technical approach to society has been joined with a focus on literal computer technology.

Much of this is good. There is nothing defensible about being indifferent to whether your programme hurts more than it helps. Textbook economics, science and public health contain important messages which are often right. We hope this book has persuaded you that the germ theory of disease deserves much of the credit for the fact that, out of every 1,000 babies that are born, 125 more survive infancy now than did fifty-five years ago.

But the implementation of this scientific knowledge has had more to do with inexpensive methods of preventing neonatal tetanus in villages than with Internet-connected hospitals in state capitals. When policymakers get excited about the promise of modern solutions, it is easy for them to overlook unfashionable, unsanitary, old problems in old places.

Throughout this book, we have learnt some surprising facts. We have also been surprised to learn that there are important missing 'facts' that nobody knows, including some basic descriptive statistics that would appear essential to public management. For example, when it is easy to download from the UN website the count and percentage of Indian persons defecating in the open in each of the last twenty-five years (to three significant digits), one gets the clear impression that somebody out there is managing it closely and has matters well in hand. The truth is altogether different: No national survey has ever measured person-level open defecation in India in any year and the UN statistics division produces each year's number by projecting forward a line drawn through household latrine ownership counts from the 2011 census, a demographic survey conducted a decade ago, and some other government survey data.

One consequence of this technocratic spirit is that it is easy to believe that all public problems are ultimately management problems, rather than political or social problems. With the right analytics and the right tools, there is nothing we cannot expect to accomplish promptly. Policymakers today do not know less than policymakers a generation ago, but they may feel like they know more than they do. As we computed above, if policymakers delay the search for solutions to the causes of India's exceptionally poor open defecation (or neonatal mortality rate or maternal nutrition) because it seems like a solved or outmoded problem, opportunities to save many lives may be irretrievably missed.

A larger reason to treat technocracy with care may be in the political trade-offs it encourages. Effectiveness and managerial competence are valuable, but they are not the only virtues in a leader. Is a good government one that cooperates with a programme of quantitative evaluation or that uses e-governance apps on tablets? It is not difficult to find historical examples of governments that were originally praised by technocratic professionals for their expertise or effectiveness that have come to be viewed as deeply ethically compromised. Nor is it difficult to understand why such a government might initially appear attractive: The Great Escape may be proceeding quickly relative to history, but change can be frustratingly slow relative to the length of a human life.

There is no reason to believe that such problematic historical cases could not be repeated today in other countries, 'developed' or 'developing', from the political left or the political right. In exchange for a promise to solve old problems, talking heads and policy wonks could yet again throw their support behind national leaders who are known as skilled managers, efficient businessmen or smart negotiators – overlooking evidence that such managerial promise or business acumen is exaggerated, and even overlooking harmful records on social equality, human rights or political violence.

Recommendation 1: Measure open defecation with independent surveys and make realistic plans

We have learnt much from the basic facts about who defecates in the open and where. We have learnt that there is much open defecation in India, compared to other developing countries. We have also learnt that variation in open defecation is not well explained by variation in poverty, education or governance; so these are unlikely to be its causes. We have learnt that many people with affordable latrines (nicer than what is standard in other developing countries) nevertheless defecate in the open and that those in rural India who do not defecate in the open instead typically use a privately constructed latrine with an extremely large pit or cement-lined tank. Almost nobody builds for themselves the simple pit latrines that are common elsewhere. And, unfortunately, we have learnt that there is enough open defecation in rural India, declining sufficiently slowly, that it is likely to exist for many years to come.

All of these facts are knowable from sample survey data – the least expensive form of statistical data to collect. They do not require a census or a large, complex randomized experiment – although both of these are tools that serve useful purposes in their contexts. Up-to-date data on open defecation can be collected through inexpensive sample surveys designed for the purpose (as we have done) or essentially for free by making small modifications to existing high-quality sample surveys (such as a Demographic and Health Survey, or India's excellent national consumption surveys run by the Ministry of Statistics and Programme Implementation). This could be done every year, or every other year, perhaps with special samples for large or important states.

A sample survey randomly selects villages and respondents to produce useful representative statistics with a quantifiable degree of sampling error. It is easy to design sampling strategies such that the sample size is feasible to collect and sampling error is acceptably small. Although we do not fully understand why, we have noticed that there is a preference among many senior bureaucrats in India for *census* data: records that claim to cover each and every person, household or village. Although such a larger database has no *sampling* error, its other disadvantages can be overwhelming. In particular, a census in India would be over 10,000 times as large as an excellent sample survey. It must therefore be collected by an enormous organization of surveyors. It would be essentially impossible to ensure quality data and supervision of such an operation with the resources potentially available for an ongoing sanitation survey. And it is absolutely unnecessary. A high-quality sample survey that sends the right surveyors to ask the right questions would be inexpensive and would produce the data needed to turn eliminating open defecation from an aspiration into a plan.

As we detailed in the previous chapter, official data on sanitation now are administrative records on latrine construction, entered by the same people whose job it is to ensure that latrines get built. While such data have their accounting purposes, they are incomplete in two important ways: They do not measure open defecation behaviour, which is the critical outcome that latrines are constructed to change; and they are not a source of information independent of local administrators. Having independent survey data would allow policymakers to allocate resources and attention responsively to places that need them and to learn credibly from places that achieve gains.

As researchers, we recognize that we may be idealistically devoted to truthfulness, but there are important practical benefits of realism in policymaking too. Projecting an image that open defecation is being quickly eliminated discards the opportunity to construct a better policy that will save more lives. Further, sanitation policy in India, unlike in some countries, is made in an electoral democracy. Realistic facts and data about sanitation policies therefore offer the extra benefits of facilitating democratic accountability and informing everybody everywhere who is rightly interested in one of the greatest human development challenges of our times.

Recommendation 2: Talk about culture, choices and caste

People make choices. Sometimes these choices hurt other people. Sometimes we hurt ourselves. Everybody makes mistakes. Everybody responds to incentives. Each human being is, from time to time, responsible for the occasional negative externality. Even poor people.

It is a challenge for many development professionals to build upon the fact that poor people sometimes behave imperfectly. When poor village elites discriminate against poor low-caste neighbours, this causes suffering. When people who could make and use a simple latrine defecate in the open instead, they are hurting their neighbours' children, even if nobody objects. Recognizing this is not 'blaming the victim' – the victims are today's babies.

Perhaps to avoid admitting that poor people have the power to choose harm, development texts often attribute unfortunate behaviours to poverty. In its Sanitation Fact Sheet, the World Health Organization writes that 'some 13 per cent of the global population is forced to defecate in the open'. In the foreword to its 2015 Report on Global Water and Sanitation, the deputy Secretary General of the UN writes that 'open defecation is one of the clearest manifestations of extreme poverty'. Neither of these claims is true. Open defecation is not concentrated among the world's poorest people. Most of the people who defecate in the open live in families that could afford to build a simple latrine. In our SQUAT survey, 84 per cent of households that did not own a latrine or toilet owned a mobile phone, and over 30 per cent owned a TV. Digging a minimally protected hole in the ground is an accessible option for most rural people. Some of the people who defecate in the open already own a latrine.

Denial of the decision-making power of the poor often takes the subtle form of quantifying 'access'. People who defecate in the open become people without 'access' to sanitation. In the fifty-one pages of the 2015 report of the WHO–UNICEF Joint Monitoring Programme, we counted seventy-nine references to 'access' to sanitation. Discussing the failure of the world to meet global sanitation targets, the report reads: 'Despite failing to meet the target of halving the proportion of the population without access, Southern Asia nevertheless managed to provide access to 32 per cent of the current population.' In this rhetoric, 'Southern Asia' acts with agency, but poor people do not.

Equating open defecation with lack of access to sanitation denies poor people the freedom to choose to defecate in the open. We wish nobody would choose to do so, but they do. This word choice matters. It misdiagnoses open defecation as a problem that can be solved merely by providing toilet parts. That means it distracts us from finding solutions. And, it obscures the humanity of poor people, whose choices are limited by poverty, but not eliminated by it. If Ashok Singh (from Chapter 4) had truly been forced by lack of access to defecate in the open, he could not have called upon his himmat to empty his latrine pit.

If acknowledging the choices of poor people that harm their poor neighbours is difficult for many in development, incorporating the effects of *culture* into authoritative texts, plans and programme designs is an even bigger challenge. For the Indian government, talking about casteism could be especially difficult. Even a bureaucrat who himself rejects casteism knows that he will principally be working through colleagues belonging to higher-ranking castes. International development organizations are more insulated from domestic politics, but there are at least two important constraints for them too.

First, many international development professionals fear that discussing the social science of culture might lead to or be confused for ethnocentrism or colonialist bias, both of which it is certainly correct to avoid. Second, even where planners working in a developing country do understand the effects of cultural differences, they are often working within large international organizations where geography is correlated with rank, so the highest bosses are most interested in solutions for everywhere.

But as understandable as these *causes* for the invisibility of culture in development may be, they are not sufficient *reasons* to ignore culture in the cases where it matters. There is no question that culture can shape behaviour in ways that cause important differences in demographic and health outcomes across populations. Son preference in South Asia has consequences for the average height and mortality of hundreds of millions of girls and boys. Alcohol consumption is recognized by demographers as an important part of exceptionally high adult mortality in Russia. The World Health Organization has claimed that burial customs, especially the washing of dead bodies, were important factors contributing to the 2014 Ebola outbreak in western Africa. Experts debate the exact details, but it is clear that the intensity of the HIV-AIDS epidemic in southern and eastern Africa is due in part to patterns of sexual partnership formation that are not as common in other populations of the world. Americans who report that religion is very important in their lives have greater actual and intended fertility than less religious Americans.

There is every reason for international development agencies and professionals to seek to carefully avoid ethnocentrism. But avoiding bias does not require denying the possibility of social and cultural facts and forces. Moreover, the problem is not only among international agencies. The Indian government's guidelines for the rural SBM use the word 'caste' only once, in the subsection titled 'Equity and Inclusion'. Yet, policymakers have learnt to talk about the importance of gender, and even about the consequences of unfortunate cultural challenges such as sex-selective abortion and female genital mutilation. These are difficult and nuanced conversations to have. We could all similarly learn to talk usefully about the continuing, slowly improving realities of caste and untouchability and purity and pollution.

Of course, people working to promote social equality will meet with political challenges, as they do in many societies. As a case study of the concentration of power, Aashish Gupta, Ankita Aggarwal and Jean Drèze investigated the caste composition of policymakers and powerful people in Allahabad: 'the Press Club, the university faculty, the Bar Association, the police, and the commanding positions in trade unions, non-governmental organizations, media houses, among other public institutions. These turn out to be heavily dominated by a small group of upper castes – Brahmins and Kayasthas in particular.' It is not clear that there is a solution to rural open defecation, built around combating casteism and norms of purity and pollution, that is also sufficiently socially and politically sanitized to be acceptable to decision makers.

———

Caste is most important to open defecation in rural India because of its consequences for the perception of latrine pits. But casteism also has implications for policy approaches to ending open defecation – commonly used in other developing countries – in which a village is intended to come together as a community and adopt a shared commitment to ending open defecation. Such approaches are correct to emphasize behaviour change over latrine construction. Sadly, however, the north Indian villages where open defecation remains common are rarely characterized by harmonious relationships. Indeed, although the word 'community' can mean 'small town' or 'geographic area' in much of the world, in Indian English it has little to do with one's physical neighbours. One's 'community' is one's caste or religious group. In the India Human Development Survey, villages that report more inter-caste conflict are the villages where more people defecate in the open, on average.

Although it may sound like splitting hairs, these examples tell us that we must distinguish between *caste* and *casteism*. It is a tragedy that Indians suffer inequality by caste: In almost every indicator, including latrine ownership, lower-caste citizens fare worse than their higher-caste neighbours. But beyond this disparity between people, there are further consequences of casteism – its ideas and its divisiveness – for everybody. One of these consequences is enduring open defecation. To their credit, many reports from government bodies and international agencies note inequalities across people and families by caste rank. The next step is to acknowledge and work against the broader costs of a casteist society.

The many dimensions of fragmentation in Indian society may have consequences that extend far beyond preventing collective action on sanitation. In *Humanity*, a long reflection on the atrocities of the twentieth century, philosopher Jonathan Glover identifies a struggle between the psychological, social and political forces of human cruelty on the one hand and what he calls 'the moral resources' on the other, in which we can place hope: psychological tendencies such as revulsion to violence, moral identities which limit the harm that people are willing to see themselves to cause to others, and human responses of sympathy. People in every society have these moral resources, but they can be defeated. Moral resources are often most effective when directed towards people 'like me', that is, towards one's in-group. So, ethical progress happens in part, as Peter Singer has argued, through an 'expanding circle' of an ever larger in-group that recognizes others as morally like oneself.

But in highly fragmented Indian society – where every other person is in some important way different due to age, gender, family role, caste or religion – the moral resources face an uphill battle. Ambedkar recognized this, in *Annihilation of Caste*:

> Caste has killed public spirit. Caste has destroyed the sense of public charity ... Virtue has become caste-ridden, and morality has become caste-bound. There is no sympathy to the deserving. There is no appreciation of the meritorious. There is no charity to the needy ... There is sympathy but not for men of other caste.

In fifty years – maybe thirty, maybe seventy – when open defecation is finally eliminated from rural India, many people will celebrate the accomplishment. For such an important achievement in the history of our species, there will be much credit to be shared among many, many people. If we are still alive, we will celebrate too. Perhaps we will live long enough to hang the colourful graphs in that shiny, bureaucratic report on our wall.

Learning to have difficult conversations about how culture and social forces influence the choices of every person, sometimes harmfully, will accelerate the coming of that day. One promising step is the most recent World Development Report of the World Bank: *Mind, Society and Behavior*, led by Karla Hoff and Varun Gauri. In this high-profile statement, the authors emphasize the importance of what people choose to do and how they understand it.

Poor people know that they are making choices that matter. The authors of the Report asked poor people in Jakarta, Nairobi and Lima whether they agree with the sentence 'What happens to me in the future mostly depends on me'. In all three cities, about 80 per cent of respondents said yes. At the same time, the authors asked World Bank staff what they believed poor people would say about themselves – these development professionals predicted that only 20 per cent of respondents would agree that they had control over their own lives. Making policy that can change behaviour like open defecation will require eliminating the gap between the influences that poor people identify as relevant to their choices and International Development's perception of what the poor are 'forced' to do.

'Human sociality is like a river running through society; it is a current constantly shaping individuals, just as flowing water shapes stones in a river bed. Policymakers can either work with these social currents or ignore them and find themselves swimming upstream.' So writes the World Development Report, but such ideas could share a bookshelf with the writings of Ambedkar. The Report ends with a call for learning how to solve new problems through iterative trial and error, informed by the thick cultural description of ethnography, by independent measurement and by mindfulness of the blind spots of development professionals.

Recommendation 3: Test and modify strategies about pollution and pits

Once open defecation is being measured and tracked, and once policymakers orient their actions around the origins of open defecation in casteism, it is time to get into the details. What exact activities should sanitation programmes in rural India do? We have some ideas, and we hope that you and many others do too. As with many policy problems, the best approaches will combine action and research, so that people can learn from and improve upon others' efforts.

If the next rural sanitation programme in India is to be more successful, we see two broad approaches it could take. It could directly confront the casteist ideas that make internationally normal latrine pits unacceptable. Or, while recognizing caste as a cause of open defecation, it could try to accommodate people's beliefs, such as by building latrines with large pits or tanks. To reach everyone, it will probably have to do both. For example, not everyone has enough land for a large underground room to store faeces.

Beyond these broad principles, what next steps should be tested? We do not know. As we wrote in the first chapter, we wrote this book to attract other people to a challenge that has humbled us. Before we proceed to our own untested ideas, there are some suggestions that we frequently hear that we do not suspect will be successful. As we wrote above, any proposal predicated on the plan that caste-fragmented Indian villages will come together to collectively end open defecation (or otherwise cooperate) is probably too long-term a hope for today's sanitation challenges. Similarly, any approach that relies upon teachers, village officials or other local leaders to quickly throw their energies into promoting latrine use (without a serious plan for changing these officials' own beliefs) will perhaps run afoul of the fact that too many teachers and leaders share other villagers' casteist views and unsanitary notions. For example, the India Human Development Survey asks people whether anyone in their household has a personal acquaintance with people from various occupations; teachers, who often come from high-ranking castes, are one of these. Rural households in which someone knows a teacher personally are no less likely to defecate in the open than households in which no one knows a teacher. Finally, it has recently become popular for public programmes to apply 'light touch' approaches from marketing or psychology to 'nudge' people into changing their behaviour – without actually changing their underlying preferences or options. However, it is no criticism of nudges that they can only solve some problems, and we fear that the problems with 'small' latrine pits are too explicitly and thoroughly grounded in many rural Indians' beliefs and goals for this strategy to succeed here. Of course, if a successful programme proved us wrong about any of these ideas, we would be nothing but delighted.

So, what next steps should be tested? The ideas we would like to see tested are built around the problems of untouchability, purity and pollution, and the misperceptions that latrine pits fill too quickly and cannot be emptied by hand. Here are a few examples:

- Teach people that latrine pits actually take much longer to fill up than they believe. If people correctly believe it will take years rather than weeks or months, more people might be willing to use the pits in ordinary government latrines.
- Teach people about affordable twin-pit latrines, including how they work, how often they need to be

emptied and why they are a good sanitation option for most places in rural India.

- Where that fails, consider spending the large latrine construction subsidy on larger pits, rather than on expensive superstructures. This might delay the need for emptying the pit until more people have grown accustomed to latrine use.
- Find a way to offer convenient and guaranteed methods of emptying latrine pits while ensuring that workers engaged in such jobs use safety gear, are well-compensated and choose such a career freely.
- Use the imagery of purity and pollution to subvert casteist constraints. Depict high-ranking villagers getting on with emptying a latrine pit safely.
- Acknowledge the continued existence of manual scavenging and address it in a meaningful way. The government should stop employing people to do work which is outlawed under the 2013 act prohibiting manual scavenging and pay to upgrade outdated urban sanitation and drainage systems. It should prosecute people who hire manual scavengers. It should also clearly make the point that emptying decomposed latrine pits is not manual scavenging.
- Above all, embrace the problem. Both the government and international development should be vocal about the causes of widespread open defecation in India. Struggling against untouchability is working towards the end of open defecation in India, and vice versa.

Where India goes

Indian children are born into a poisonous environment. Faecal germs threaten their survival and their physical and cognitive development. Caste hierarchies make what would otherwise be an ordinary project of sanitary engineering into an enduring drain on human development and well-being. Even if a quick fix emerged today, open defecation's effects will be with us at least until people who were exposed to open defecation in infancy age through their lives.

Unfortunately, policymakers should not expect a quick fix. Much of the slow reduction in open defecation that has already been achieved has been due to gradual urbanization, itself slowed by caste and by social networks which encourage people to remain in villages. The latrines that are used in rural India are so expensive that they reinforce the very purity and pollution norms that higher-caste people use to assert their social dominance over lower-caste people. The hypothetical interventions that seem to us most likely to accelerate the reduction of open defecation take the challenges presented by caste and untouchability head on. But just as the terrible legacy and continuing toll of racism in countries like the US, Brazil and South Africa heal only excruciatingly slowly, the scars of untouchability will not fade overnight.

This is where our book ends. It is not too late for the continuing story of open defecation in India to have a happier ending. Anyone working to accelerate the decline of open defecation in rural India should start thinking about how to convince people to use affordable latrines – in many cases, the ones the government is already happy to build – and how to accelerate the shift to a less divided society. Promoting social equality is indeed a more difficult path to eliminating open defecation than the ones that other countries have faced. Lest this fact seem discouraging, it will also have much greater benefits.

Notes

In reporting our qualitative evidence from field research, we have changed identifiable names of persons and certain local places for anonymity, attempting to preserve what is implied about social status, demographic categories and geography. All such persons, places and events refer to a specific individual or instance: No narrative composites are used. We use 'we' to refer to something we both, Diane and Dean, did together, unless the context makes clear that one of us was acting with another person.

Some important data sources are drawn upon through the book:

SQUAT Survey. With our r.i.c.e. colleagues, we collected the SQUAT survey from November 2013 through March 2014. The survey data and questionnaires are publicly available at www.riceinstitute.org. Details on the sample design and methodology are available online in SQUAT Working Paper No. 1, part of which was published as: Coffey, D., A. Gupta, P. Hathi, N. Khurana, D. Spears, N. Srivastav and S. Vyas, 2014. 'Revealed preference for open defecation', *Economic & Political Weekly*, Vol. 49, No. 38, p. 43.

Qualitative field research. In addition to the unstructured learning we have done throughout our time in rural India, with our r.i.c.e. colleagues, we conducted a formal set of in-depth, semi-structured qualitative interviews in Valsad district of Gujarat, Rewari district of Haryana, Fatehpur district of Uttar Pradesh and Parsa district of southern Nepal. The authors also did extensive pre-testing of the interview guide in Sitapur district of Uttar Pradesh and follow-up fieldwork in Jaipur, Rajasthan; Sitapur, Uttar Pradesh; Muzaffarpur and Sheohar districts of Bihar; and Tiruvannamalai and Vellore districts of Tamil Nadu. Details on the field site selection and methodology are available in:

Coffey, D., A. Gupta, P. Hathi, N. Khurana, D. Spears, N. Srivastav and S. Vyas, 2017. 'Understanding open defecation in rural India: Untouchability, pollution, and latrine pits', *Economic & Political Weekly*, Special Issue: Rural Affairs.

DHS. Whenever we refer to DHS data or to undifferentiated 'demographic surveys', we mean the Demographic and Health Surveys, known in India as the National Family Health Survey (NFHS). It is publicly available at www.measuredhs.com

IHDS. We frequently report our tabulations from the India Human Development Survey (IHDS). The IHDS is a nationally representative panel of approximately 40,000 households collected in 2005 and 2012 by a collaboration between National Council for Applied Economics Research (NCAER) and the University of Maryland, under principal investigators Sonalde Desai and Reeve Vanneman. It is publicly available at ihds.info

JMP. Otherwise unattributed statistics about open defecation in countries other than India are from the UNICEF–WHO Joint Monitoring Programme, online at www.wssinfo.org. These are estimates that the JMP produces by estimating time trends from statistical data collected by country governments (such as census data), by the DHS or by WHO or UNICEF surveys.

Many of the notes below are full citations to works or authors mentioned in the text. In cases where we are elaborating on a point in the text, or where the text did not mention the name of the author, we provide the page number and a few words from the text in **boldface** to help the reader match the note.

Chapter 1

- **p. 5: international trend predicts.** A cross-country regression, based on GDP per capita, predicts that India would have an infant mortality rate (IMR) of 36.0, compared with the observed 42.6. Assuming a little over twenty-seven million births per year (the latest figure from the United Nations is 27.2 million in 2010), this difference multiplies to 178,000 deaths that would be averted if India had an IMR of 36. This gap is about 4 per cent of the entire global count of 4.5 million infant deaths per year. In 2015, the WHO Global Health Observatory data repository reports that 190 million infants died in the Americas (over thirty countries, including the US and Brazil). Thus, India's infant mortality in excess of what its GDP per capita predicts is 94 per cent of the total count of infant deaths in the Americas.
- **p. 5: more than one in five infant deaths.** 946 in India ÷ 4,450 globally, in thousands, from *Levels & Trends in Child Mortality Report 2015: Estimates Developed by the UN Inter-agency Group for Child Mortality Estimation.* For under-five mortality the fraction is similar: 1,348 (India) ÷ 6,395 (world).
- Ramalingaswami, V., U. Jonsson and J. Rohde, 1997. Malnutrition: A South Asian Enigma, UNICEF.
- Drèze, J. and A. Sen, 2013. *An Uncertain Glory: India and Its Contradictions*, Princeton: Princeton University Press.
- **p. 9: globally special case that helps us understand how social inequality constrains human development.** Distinctions of social hierarchy pervade Indian society, especially in the north Indian villages where open defecation is most common. Of course, sanitation is far from the only way in which social forces constrain India's human development. For example, maternal nutrition is so poor that the average mother in India

ends pregnancy weighing less than the average mother in sub-Saharan Africa does at the beginning of pregnancy. One important reason for such high levels of maternal malnutrition in India is social inequality among older and younger men and women: Young, childbearing-age women are low-ranking within their households. This means that they eat less than other family members, even during the special nutritional needs of pregnancy. As a result, young mothers weigh much less than older, higher-ranking women. As profoundly deficient as India's maternal nutrition is, and as pervasive as the effects of India's social hierarchy are, we cannot exhaust the consequences of social inequality in this book; instead we concentrate on one significant and telling case. See Coffey, D., 2015. 'Prepregnancy body mass and weight gain during pregnancy in India and sub-Saharan Africa', *Proceedings of the National Academy of Sciences*, Vol. 112, No. 11, pp. 3302–07.

- Fogel, R.W., 2004. *The Escape from Hunger and Premature Death, 1700–2100: Europe, America, and the Third World*, Cambridge University Press.
- Deaton, A., 2013. *The Great Escape: Health, Wealth, and the Origins of Inequality*, Princeton: Princeton University Press.
- **p. 13: sanitation was an undeniably central part**. Cutler, D. and G. Miller, 2005. 'The role of public health improvements in health advances: The twentieth-century United States', *Demography*, Vol. 42, No. 1, pp.1–22. See also: Ferriman, A., 2007. 'BMJ readers choose the "sanitary revolution" as greatest medical advance since 1840', *BMJ: British Medical Journal*, Vol. 334, No. 7585, p. 111.

Chapter 2

- International comparisons in this chapter draw heavily on Demographic and Health Surveys, on the World Bank World Development Indicators and on the JMP.
  - Figure 1, GDP per capita: World Bank World Development Indicators, International Comparison Program (ICP).

o Figure 2, Poverty: World Bank World Development Indicators.

o Figure 3, Water: UNICEF–WHO JMP. Using countrywide averages that combine urban and rural places show a downward slope because of an urban–rural composition effect: Open defecation is less common and water is more available in urban places; so urbanization rates confound the correlation between water and sanitation.

o Figure 5, Difficulty doing business rating: World Bank World Development Indicators.

• **p. 33: districts.** As of 2016 there are 686 districts in India, so the average district has a population of almost two million people. Sitapur district, where we did the field research in Uttar Pradesh for several years, has a population of about 4.5 million people in the 2011 census. To a reader familiar with the United States, districts are roughly equivalent to counties, in that they are administrative divisions of states which largely receive their resources and authority from state governments.

• **p. 36: rural people in other countries.** Households that did not have piped water on the premises also told census enumerators whether their water source was 'near' or 'far'. After categorizing the households by what else they own, to separate differences in economic position from differences in water access, there is no association between whether similarly rich or poor households have a 'near' or 'far' water source and whether the households own a latrine.

• polity database: 'Polity IV Project: Political Regime Characteristics and Transitions, 1800–2013.' Monty G. Marshall, Principal Investigator; Ted Robert Gurr, Founder. http://www.systemicpeace.org/polity/polity4.htm

• **p. 40: a UN website.** http://www.un.org/waterforlifedecade/sanitation.html. The title of the page given by the website menu is 'Access to sanitation'.

• Spears, D. and A. Thorat, 2017. 'Caste, purity, and pollution and the puzzle of open defecation in India: Evidence from a novel measure in a nationally-representative survey', *Economic Development and Cultural Change*.

- **p. 42: behaviour of individual family members.** To be clear, this is not necessarily a defect of the DHS: It uses a standardized survey form for developing countries around the world. It is reasonable that researchers who wrote the first DHS surveys for Latin America and Africa in the 1980s would not have taken into account that decades later many people in India might live in households in which some people use a latrine and others do not. Just the same, it is a good example of the maxim that the same survey questions may not always work in all societies.
- **p. 42: our team at r.i.c.e.** The team that led the SQUAT survey was Diane Coffey, Aashish Gupta, Payal Hathi, Nidhi Khurana, Dean Spears, Nikhil Srivastav and Sangita Vyas. We could never have done it without the field leadership of Nidhi and Aashish.
- **p. 43: find more of it.** One question the SQUAT data raises is how big a difference measuring person-level behaviour rather than household-level behaviour makes to aggregate summary statistics on open defecation. In our sample, the fraction of *people* who defecate in the open was 12 percentage points larger than the fraction of *households* that do not own latrines. Of course, the difference between rates of open defecation at the person level and those at the household level would not be so for the whole country: Our sample weights Haryana, which has a lot of latrines, and a lot of people who do not use them, the same as Uttar Pradesh and Bihar, which have a lot more people, and a lot more households without a latrine. Nevertheless, the fraction of persons who defecate in the open is higher than the fraction of households who do not own a latrine. This difference is likely to become greater as more households construct toilets.
- **p. 43: working latrine.** In order to compute this statistic, we determined that a household had a 'working latrine' if someone in the household used a latrine on the household's

land, or if there was a latrine structure with both a pit and a pan. The results are not importantly different if we look only at households in which at least one person is using the latrine, thereby excluding cases in which our surveyors made any sort of judgement about whether a latrine was functional.

- Hueso, A. and B. Bell, 2013. 'An untold story of policy failure: The Total Sanitation Campaign in India', *Water Policy*, Vol. 15, No. 6, pp. 1001–1017.
- Coffey, D., A. Gupta, P. Hathi, N. Khurana, D. Spears, N. Srivastav and S. Vyas, 2014. 'Revealed Preference for Open Defecation', *Economic & Political Weekly*, Vol. 49, No. 38, p. 43.
- Clasen, T., S. Boisson, P. Routray, B. Torondel, M. Bell, O. Cumming, J. Ensink, M. Freeman, M. Jenkins, M. Odagiri and S. Ray, 2014. 'Effectiveness of a rural sanitation programme on diarrhoea, soil-transmitted helminth infection, and child malnutrition in Odisha, India: A cluster-randomised trial', *Lancet Global Health*, Vol. 2, No. 11, pp. e645–e653.
- **p. 44: Indian government has been subsidizing latrines in villages for more than three decades.** In his book *Health and Population in South Asia: From Earliest Times to the Present*, Sumit Guha points out that government latrines were built in some villages of West Bengal as early as the late 1940s. He cites a *Report of the Environment Hygiene Committee of 1949*, which says that 'The provision of latrines in villages is beset with many difficulties. The villagers themselves do not want them in the first place and build them only to humour the health officer or the officials whom they do not want to displease.'

Chapter 3

- Khare, R.S., 1962. 'Ritual purity and pollution in relation to domestic sanitation', the *Eastern Anthropologist*, Vol. 15, No. 2.
- Srinivas, M.N. 1976. *The Remembered Village*, Oxford University Press.

- Gupta, D., 2005. 'Caste and politics: Identity over system', *Annual Review of Anthropology*, Vol. 34, pp. 409–427.
- Coffey, D. 2014. 'Costs and consequences of a cash transfer for hospital births in a rural district of Uttar Pradesh', *Social Science & Medicine*.
- Thorat, A. and O. Joshi, 2015. 'The Continuing Practice of Untouchability in India: Patterns and Mitigating Influences', India Human Development Survey Working Paper 2015-2.
- **p. 56: This is not true.** Rema Hanna and Leigh Linden conducted an audit experiment in urban India, where they put different cover sheets over the same exam papers, randomly assigning the caste of the student that the grader would see on the cover sheet. Teachers who were implicitly told that the test belonged to a lower-caste student gave lower marks, on average, than teachers who were told that the test belonged to a higher-caste student – even though the 'responses' to the tests were the same. In their experiment, Hanna and Linden did not assign caste names as low-ranking as Dalits – presumably discrimination against these lowest-ranked students could be even more severe. See: Hanna, R.N. and L.L. Linden, 2012. 'Discrimination in grading', *American Economic Journal: Economic Policy*, Vol. 4, No. 4, pp. 146–168.
- Pinto, S., 2003. 'Casting desire: Reproduction, loss and subjectivity in rural north India', Doctoral dissertation, Princeton University.
- Lüthi, D., 2010. 'Private Cleanliness, Public Mess: Purity, Pollution and Space in Kottar, South India', *Urban Pollution: Cultural Meanings, Social Practices*, Vol. 15, p. 57.
- Teltumbde, A., 2014. 'No Swachh Bharat without Annihilation of Caste', *Economic & Political Weekly*, Vol. 49, No. 45, p. 12.
- Srinivas, M.N. 1952. *Religion and Society among the Coorgs of South India*, Oxford University Press.
- Valmiki, O., 2008. *Joothan: An Untouchable's Life*. translated by A.P. Mukherjee, Columbia University Press.

- André Béteille quoted in: Das Gupta, M., 26 June 2016. 'Not So Swachh: Indian Men Less Likely to Use Toilets Even If Available', *Hindustan Times*.
- Lamba, S. and D. Spears, 2013. 'Caste, "cleanliness" and cash: Effects of caste-based political reservations in Rajasthan on a sanitation prize', *Journal of Development Studies*, Vol. 49, No. 11, pp. 1592–1606.
- Gupta, A., D. Coffey and D. Spears, 2016. 'Purity, pollution, and untouchability: Challenges affecting the adoption, use, and sustainability of sanitation programmes in rural India', *Sustainable Sanitation for All: Experiences, Challenges, and Innovations*. Also see other chapters in that book for a contrast with issues emphasized by sanitation professionals working in other parts of the developing world.

Chapter 4

- **p. 68: promoting child growth.** We have often heard people ask whether latrine pits contaminate drinking water. Engineers and public health professionals agree that when latrines are properly constructed, they do not. This is because the soil acts as a filter that prevents faecal pathogens from travelling very far through the ground. If the latrine is built far enough from a water source, there is little risk that latrine pits will contaminate drinking water.
- **p. 69: into a tank on his truck.** We use the term 'cement-lined tank' or simply 'large pit' to refer to the underground storage containers that are used to contain faeces. These are often mistermed 'septic tanks' by masons, villagers and even government officials in India. For example, a letter to District Collectors and other officials from the Tamil Nadu Director of Rural Development and Panchayati Raj writes: 'Though Septic Tanks are generally discouraged, still it is being constructed. Further, Septic Tanks are constructed like Storage Tanks.' However, a sanitation engineer would understand a septic tank

to be a potentially smaller, often multi-chambered system to store and treat one household's faecal sludge. A true septic tank is therefore a more hygienic option than the cement-lined tanks that are used in many places in India.

- Feachem, R., D. D. Mara and D. J. Bradley, 1983. *Sanitation and Disease: Health Aspects of Excreta and Wastewater Management*, John Wiley & Sons.
- WHO 1996. *Simple pit latrines*, technical report, World Health Organization, available at www.who.int/water_sanitation_health/hygiene/emergencies/fs3_4.pdf
- Price of high-quality Bangladeshi latrines: Guiteras, R., J. Levinsohn and A.M. Mobarak, 2015. 'Encouraging sanitation investment in the developing world: A cluster-randomized trial', *Science*, Vol. 348, No. 6337, pp. 903–906.
- Government of India, 2012. 'Houses, Household Amenities and Assets', Census 2011, New Delhi.
- Ambedkar, B.R. 1935. 'The Revolt of the Untouchables', *Dr. Babasaheb Ambedkar: Writings & Speeches*, Volume 5, Education Department, Government of Maharashtra.
- Pisharoty, Sangeeta Barooah, 2016. 'Twenty-three years since Anti-Manual Scavenging Act not much has changed on ground', April, *The Wire*, available at http://thewire.in/28833/twenty-three-years-since-anti-manual-scavenging-act-but-not-much-has-changed-on-ground/
- National Crime Records Bureau, 2014. 'Crime against Persons Belonging to SCs/STs', *Crime in India, 2014: Compendium*, Chapter 7, New Delhi, Ministry of Home Affairs, Government of India.
- **p. 77: this dangerous work.** One important example of the government hiring manual scavengers is the Indian Railways, which employs people to clean human faeces off train tracks because most train toilets do not collect human waste. A 2014 Human Rights Watch report found that over 7,000 trains in India dispose of faeces directly on to the tracks every day.

Instead of hiring people to clean the tracks, the government could install proper toilets in the trains and employ people to safely dispose of the faeces using machines. See: Human Rights Watch, 2014. *Cleaning Human Waste: Manual Scavenging, Caste and Discrimination in India.*

- Government-sponsored manual scavenging also happens when towns and cities hire people to de-sludge drains into which latrines empty or people defecate directly. De-sludging drains is hazardous not only to the health of those manual scavengers who perform it, but also to everyone who is exposed to germs that are spread [of CLTS] when the sludge inevitably gets on people's shoes or is carried by flies. In the district capital town of Sitapur in Uttar Pradesh, we have often seen the busiest roads in town lined with piles of fresh sludge. The sludge is manually removed from the drains and left to dry between the drains and the doors of houses or businesses, in exactly the places where people normally walk.
- Ambedkar, B.R., 1936. *Annihilation of Caste.*
- Shah, G. *et al.*, 2006. *Untouchability in Rural India*, New Delhi: Sage.
- Ashok Singh's three-foot pit: Some local government officials have told us that they suggest three-foot-deep latrine pits so that a person who is emptying the pit by hand does not have to enter the pit to remove the sludge.
- Spears, D. and A. Thorat, 2017. 'Caste, purity, and pollution and the puzzle of open defecation in India: Evidence from a novel measure in a nationally-representative survey', *Economic Development and Cultural Change.*

Chapter 5

- Preston, S.H., 1975. 'The changing relation between mortality and level of economic development', *Population Studies*, Vol. 29, No. 2, pp. 231–248.

- Ghosh, A., A. Gupta and D. Spears, 2014. 'Are children in West Bengal shorter than children in Bangladesh?', *Economic & Political Weekly*, Vol. 48.
- Bhalotra, S., C. Valente and A. van Soest, 2010. 'The puzzle of Muslim Advantage in child survival in India', *Journal of Health Economics*, Vol. 29, No. 2, pp. 191–204.
- Geruso, M. and D. Spears, 2015. 'Neighbourhood Sanitation and Infant Mortality', Working paper no. W 21184, National Bureau of Economic Research. This research, as well as the height research in this chapter, uses the nationally representative data of the Ministry of Health and Family Welfare's National Family Health Survey (NFHS), which is India's version of the internationally comparable Demographic and Health Surveys (DHS). In the most recent round, 2005–6, '18 research organisations conducted interviews with more than 230,000 women age 15-49 and men age 15-54 throughout India', according to the website of the International Institute for Population Sciences, designated as the nodal agency for the survey.
- **p. 106: only 164 centimetres tall.** Data on the heights of adult men in OECD countries, including Japan, is available from 'Society at a Glance: OECD Social Indicators'. We computed the heights of adult men in India using the 2005-6 NFHS /DHS.
- **p. 106: children in China.** China has never had a Demographic and Health Survey, but the China Health and Nutrition Survey shows that the average child in China is about three-fourths of a standard deviation below the WHO reference norms, compared with a gap of 1.5 to 2 in India.
- Bogin, B., 1999. *Patterns of Human Growth*, Cambridge University Press.
- Proos, L.A., Y. Hofvander and T. Tuvemo, 1991. Menarcheal Age and Growth Pattern of Indian Girls Adopted in Sweden: 'I. Menarcheal Age', *Acta Paediatrica*, Vol. 80, No. 1, pp. 852–858.
- Proos, L.A., Y. Hofvander, K. Wennqvist and T. Tuvemo, 1992. 'A longitudinal study on anthropometric and clinical development of Indian children adopted in Sweden: II.

Growth, morbidity and development during two years after arrival in Sweden', *Uppsala Journal of Medical Sciences*, Vol. 97, No. 1, pp. 93–106.

- Hatton, T.J., 2013. 'How have Europeans grown so tall?', *Oxford Economic Papers*.

- **p. 108: occurred rapidly in South Korea.** Schwekendiek, D. and S. Pak, 2009. 'Recent growth of children in the two Koreas: A meta-analysis', *Economics & Human Biology*, Vol. 7, No. 1, pp. 109–112.

- Coffey, D., A. Deaton, J. Drèze, D. Spears and A. Tarozzi, 2013. 'Stunting among children: Facts and implications', *Economic & Political Weekly*, Vol. 48, No. 34, p. 69.

- Bhandari, N., R. Bahl, S. Taneja, M.D. Onis and M.K. Bhan, 2002. 'Growth performance of affluent Indian children is similar to that in developed countries', *Bulletin of the World Health Organization*, Vol. 80, No. 3, pp. 189–195.

- Humphrey, J.H., 2009. 'Child undernutrition, tropical enteropathy, toilets, and handwashing', *The Lancet*, Vol. 374, No. 9694, pp. 1032–35.

- Prendergast, A.J., S. Rukobo, B. Chasekwa, K. Mutasa, R. Ntozini, M.N. Mbuya, A. Jones, L.H. Moulton, R.J. Stoltzfus and J.H. Humphrey, 2014. 'Stunting is characterized by chronic inflammation in Zimbabwean infants', *PLoS one*, Vol. 9, No. 2, p. e86928.

- Lin, A., B.F. Arnold, S. Afreen, R. Goto, T.M.N. Huda, R. Haque, R. Raqib, L. Unicomb, T. Ahmed, J.M. Colford and S.P. Luby, 2013. 'Household environmental conditions are associated with enteropathy and impaired growth in rural Bangladesh', *The American Journal of Tropical Medicine and Hygiene*, Vol. 89, No. 1, pp. 130–137.

- Coffey, D., M. Geruso and D. Spears, 2017. 'Sanitation, Disease, and Anemia: Evidence from Nepal', *The Economic Journal*.

- Spears, D., 2013. 'How much international variation in child height can sanitation explain?', World Bank Policy Research, Working Paper No. 6351.

- Spears, D., A. Ghosh and O. Cumming, 2013. 'Open defecation and childhood stunting in India: An ecological analysis of new data from 112 districts', *PLoS one*, Vol. 8, No. 9, p. e73784.
- Spears, D., 2015. 'Lessons from recent literature and the IHDS', *Undernutrition and Public Policy in India: Investing in the Future*, Routledge, p. 79.
- Spears, D. and L.J. Haddad, 2015. 'The power of WASH: Why sanitation matters for nutrition', *IFPRI Global Food Policy Report*, pp. 19–24.
- Gertler, P., M. Shah, M.L. Alzua, L. Cameron, S. Martinez and S. Patil, 2015. 'How does health promotion work? Evidence from the dirty business of eliminating open defecation', Working Paper No. W20997. National Bureau of Economic Research.
- Hammer, J. and D. Spears, 2016. 'Village sanitation and child health: Effects and external validity in a randomized field experiment in rural India', *Journal of Health Economics*, Vol. 48, pp. 135–148.
- Hathi, P., S. Haque, L. Pant, D. Coffey and D. Spears, 2017. 'Place and child health: The interaction of population density and sanitation in developing countries', *Demography*.

Chapter 6

- Figure 7 is reprinted from Spears, D., *Economics & Human Biology*, copyright 2012, with permission from Elsevier; licence number 3897271424972.
- Becker, G.S., 1962. 'Investment in human capital: A theoretical analysis', *Journal of Political Economy*, pp. 9–49.
- Currie, J. and T. Vogl, 2013. 'Early-Life Health and Adult Circumstance in Developing Countries', *Annual Review of Economics*, Vol. 5, pp. 1–36.
- Maluccio, J.A., J. Hoddinott, J.R. Behrman, R. Martorell, A.R. Quisumbing and A.D. Stein, 2009. 'The impact of improving nutrition during early childhood on education among

Guatemalan adults', *The Economic Journal*, Vol. 119, No. 537, pp.734–763.

- Case, A. and C. Paxson, 2008. 'Stature and Status: Height, Ability, and Labor Market Outcomes', *Journal of Political Economy*, Vol. 116, No. 3.
- Case, A. and C. Paxson, 2010. 'Causes and consequences of early-life health', *Demography*, Vol. 47, No. 1, pp. S65–S85.
- Spears, D., 2012. 'Height and cognitive achievement among Indian children.' *Economics & Human Biology*, Vol. 10, No. 2, pp. 210–219.
- Vogl, T.S., 2014. 'Height, skills, and labor market outcomes in Mexico', *Journal of Development Economics*, Vol. 107, pp. 84–96.
- Bleakley, H., 2007. 'Disease and development: Evidence from hookworm eradication in the American South', *Quarterly Journal of Economics*, Vol. 122, No. 1, p. 73.
- Spears, D. and S. Lamba, 2016. 'Effects of Early-Life Exposure to Sanitation on Childhood Cognitive Skills: Evidence from India's Total Sanitation Campaign', *Journal of Human Resources*, Vol. 51, No. 2, pp. 298–327.
- The Annual Status of Education Report is online at www. asercentre.org
- Flagship report: Economist Karthik Muralidharan explains ...: Presentation at 2016 International Growth Centre and Indian Statistical Institute conference in Delhi.
- Economic Impacts of Inadequate Sanitation in India, 2011. World Bank Water and Sanitation Programme.
- Cutler, D., W. Fung, M. Kremer, M. Singhal and T. Vogl, 2010. 'Early-life malaria exposure and adult outcomes: Evidence from malaria eradication in India', *American Economic Journal: Applied Economics*, Vol. 2, No. 2, pp. 72–94.
- Bleakley, H., 2010. 'Malaria eradication in the Americas: A retrospective analysis of childhood exposure', *American Economic Journal: Applied Economics*, Vol. 2, No. 2, pp. 1–45.

- Lawson, N. and D. Spears, 2016. 'What doesn't kill you makes you poorer: Adult wages and early-life mortality in India', *Economics & Human Biology*, Vol. 21, pp. 1–16.
- Subramanian, S. and A. Deaton, 1996. 'The demand for food and calories', *Journal of Political Economy*, pp. 133–162.
- Deaton, A. and J. Drèze, 2009. 'Food and nutrition in India: Facts and interpretations', *Economic & Political Weekly*, pp. 42–65.
- Duh, J. and D. Spears, 2017. 'Health and hunger: Disease, energy needs, and the Indian calorie consumption puzzle', *The Economic Journal*, forthcoming.
- Eli, S. and N. Li, 2015. 'Caloric Requirements and Food Consumption Patterns of the Poor.' Working Paper No. 21697, National Bureau of Economic Research.

Chapter 7

- **p. 157: the whole story.** For the relevant news coverage, see:
  - o APF. 1 June 2014. 'Badaun girls' tragic story points to risks women face in rural India', *Hindustan Times.*
  - o Biswas, Soutik. 30 May 2014. 'Why India's sanitation crisis kills women', BBC news.
  - o Chatterjee, Pritha. 8 June 2014. 'Going to toilet in Badaun's Katra Sadatgan: Fear, shame and discomfort grip village women', the *Indian Express.*
  - o Joshi, Sandeep. 1 September 2014. 'Sulabh begins "toilet for every house" drive from Badaun', the *Hindu.*
  - o ET Bureau. 5 June 2014. 'United Nations chief Ban Ki-moon appalled by Badaun rape case, demands action', the *Economic Times.*
  - o Chowdhury, Sagnik. 28 November 2014. 'Badaun case: Cousins committed suicide after one caught in "intimate" act, says CBI', the *Indian Express.*
  - o Bhalla, Nita. 27 November 2014. 'CBI says girls found hanging from tree in Badaun killed themselves', *Reuters.*
  - o Chatterjee, Pritha. 29 November 2014. 'Badaun case: Why few are buying CBI's suicide story', the *Indian Express.*

- **p. 159: more likely than men to invest in latrines.** Dean and Sneha Lamba have studied this in the case of Rajasthani villages, taking advantage of the fact that reservations in local government positions created an unintended social experiment to learn from. Villages that were randomly assigned to be required to have a Dalit village political chair were less likely to go on to win the Total Sanitation Campaign's clean village prize. However, villages that were randomly assigned to be required to have a female sarpanch were not more or less likely to win the prize, which in part required eliminating open defecation. Of course, winning the prize is an imperfect measure of the policy choices of the village leader and of the village's willingness to follow (after all, the prize itself may be politicized by the state government). But this test case unambiguously failed to show any evidence that women would make special investments in sanitation. See: Lamba, S. and D. Spears, 2013. 'Caste, "cleanliness" and cash: Effects of caste-based political reservations in Rajasthan on a sanitation prize', *Journal of Development Studies*, Vol. 49, No. 11, pp. 1592–1606.
- **p. 161: femininity.** Women are also less likely to talk about the benefits of open defecation for bodily purity. This may be because they are considered a 'polluted sex': Female ritual pollution, which has been widely discussed by anthropologists and sociologists, is linked to the fact that women menstruate, and is related to their low social position.
- Routray, P., B. Torondel, T. Clasen and W. P. Schmidt, 2017. 'Women's role in sanitation decision making in rural coastal Odisha, India'. *PloS one*, Vol. 12, No. 5, e0178042.

Chapter 8

- Pritchett, L., 2009. 'The Policy Irrelevance of the Economics of Education: Is "Normative as Positive" Just Useless, or Worse?', *What Works in Development*, 130–73.
- **p. 178: Quantitatively, such an accomplishment would be unprecedented.** Sanitation is not the only sector in Indian

policymaking where unrealistic quantitative 'targets' are announced; a similar computation about the plausibility of a promised pace of accomplishments in nuclear energy is presented by Ramana. See: Ramana, M.V., 2012. *The Power of Promise: Examining Nuclear Energy in India.* Penguin.

- **p. 180: Rashtriya Swachhata Kosh.** These numbers do not include a 250 crore loan for SBM from the World Bank. Nor do they include untied funds that states receive from Central taxes. In a personal communication, Accountability Initiative shared a preliminary analysis of increases in water and sanitation budgets in six states following a 2015 increase in the Central tax money transferred to states as 'untied funds'. Although it is too early to know how this change in funding mechanisms will affect spending on latrine construction, the Accountability Initiative analysis suggests that untied funds will not make up the gap between the approximately 9000 crore per year that the Centre currently spends on sanitation and the 30,000 crore per year required to build 67,000 latrines at a cost of 12,000 rupees per year.

- **p. 186: similar statistical websites.** To be sure, the administrative records on latrine construction collected by the Total Sanitation Campaign – the Central government sanitation programme of the 2000s – were positively correlated with district-level changes in latrine ownership between the 2001 and 2011 censuses of India. These census data are widely believed to be reliable about what they measure, and they suggest that these government records were correlated with the truth. They also predict health outcomes in a way that would be difficult to understand if there were not a signal amidst the noise. Places that reported building more latrines over this decade probably did tend to build more latrines over this decade, on average. But while 'correlated with the truth' about latrine construction might be all an econometric *researcher* needs in order to write an article; it is not enough for a *manager* attempting to direct a complex programme. Most importantly, the system only monitors latrine construction. It makes no effort to assess what really matters: open defecation behaviour.

- **p. 187: by whether forms are filled.** For example, Format F39, on the Swachh Bharat Mission website, is the 'Status of ODF GPs', meaning a count of villages which the state has declared 'open defecation free'. Clicking on any blue number moves to a new page, listing block, district and village names. A note reveals that these data are not about open defecation behaviour at all: 'ODF data is dynamic based on 100% toilet coverage (individual or access to public/community toilet).' In other words, as soon as a computer operator in the local capital city logs on and records that a toilet has been built for every household in a village, it automatically appears on this list. There is no verification of latrine use.

- Gilens, M. and Page, B.I., 2014. 'Testing theories of American politics: Elites, interest groups, and average citizens', *Perspectives on Politics*, Vol. 12, No. 03, pp. 564–581.

- Cornwall, A. and Brock, K., 2005. 'What do buzzwords do for development policy?', A critical look at "participation", "empowerment" and "poverty reduction"', *Third World Quarterly*, Vol. 26, No. 7, pp. 1043–1060.

- Scott, J.C., 1998. *Seeing Like a State: How Certain Schemes to Improve the Human Condition Have Failed.* Yale University Press.

- Jenkins, M.W. and V. Curtis, 2005. 'Achieving the "good life": Why some people want latrines in rural Benin', *Social Science & Medicine*, Vol. 61, No. 11, pp. 2446–2459.

- Rosenboom, J.W., C. Jacks, K. Phyrum, M. Roberts and T. Baker, 2011. 'Sanitation marketing in Cambodia', *Waterlines*, Vol. 30, No.1, pp. 21–40.

- **p. 190: not originally by the Bangladesh government.** Although not originally developed by the Bangladesh government, CLTS eventually became officially endorsed as an approach to sanitation policy. As the CLTS Knowledge Hub summarizes,

'CLTS was pioneered by Kamal Kar (a development consultant from India) together with VERC (Village Education Resource Centre), a partner of WaterAid Bangladesh, in 2000 in Mosmoil, a village in the Rajshahi district of Bangladesh, whilst evaluating a traditionally subsidised sanitation programme ... The Water and Sanitation Programme (WSP) of the World Bank played an important role in enabling spread to neighbouring India and then subsequently to Indonesia and parts of Africa. Over time, many other organisations have become important disseminators and champions of CLTS, amongst them Plan International, UNICEF, WaterAid, SNV, WSSCC, Tearfund, Care, WSP, World Vision and others. Today CLTS is in more than 60 countries in Asia, Africa, Latin America, the Pacific and the Middle East, and governments are increasingly taking the lead in scaling up CLTS. Many governments have also adopted CLTS as national policy.'

- **p. 190: one World Bank policy brief.** 'Making sanitation marketing work: The Bangladesh story', WSP. December 2013.
- Guiteras, R., J. Levinsohn and A.M. Mobarak, 2015. 'Encouraging sanitation investment in the developing world: A cluster-randomized trial.' *Science*, Vol. 348, No. 6237, pp. 903–906.
- **p. 194: The amount that is in fact spent on behaviour change is even less than this.** 'Out of the national allocation ..., 8% is to be utilised on [Information and Education Campaign] activities. 3% is to be utilized at the Central level [Ministry of Drinking Water and Sanitation] on a national pan India campaign. This shall highlight national priorities on sanitation hygiene and cleanliness. In the States, 5% of allocation shall be used on [three acronyms for Information and Education Campaigns/Behaviour Change Communication/and Inter-Personal Communication] and all related Communication activities and on Capacity building.'
- **p. 196: public employees.** This problem is not limited to sanitation. Dubash and Joseph make a similar point about the

human resources devoted to climate change policy for India: 'Even in the core nodal agency of MoEF, full-time employees focused on climate change in the Climate Change Unit are a section officer, three scientists, a director and a joint secretary (the latter also handling the Montreal Protocol), adding to six full-time staff.' Dubash, N.K. and N.B. Joseph, 2016. 'Evolution of Institutions for Climate Policy in India', *Economic & Political Weekly*, Vol. 51, No.3, p. 45.

- Pritchett, L., 2009. 'Is India a flailing state? Detours on the four lane highway to modernization'.
- **p. 195: same population size and infant mortality rate as Sierra Leone or Liberia.** With a population of 4.5 million people in the 2011 census, Sitapur district fell between the 4.2 million and 5.9 million of Liberia and Sierra Leone, respectively. According to DHS data, 73 per 1,000 babies born die before their first birthday in Liberia, and 89 do in Sierra Leone. Sitapur, according to the Annual Health Survey (AHS), is again in the middle, with an infant mortality rate of 82. Moreover, according to the same AHS data, out of the only nine states surveyed, eighteen other districts suffer infant mortality as high as Sitapur's or higher, and eight of these cases exceed even Sierra Leone's. Of course, there is nothing making Liberia or Sierra Leone especially appropriate comparison cases; they simply have similarly sized populations.
- Devarajan, S. 17 September 2013. 'Why I blog', http://blogs. worldbank.org/futuredevelopment/why-i-blog
  (Note especially the excellent discussion in the comments.)
- **p. 206: international development … administrative statistics.** Producing politically unsanitized descriptive statistics may, however, come at a political cost to international development organizations. In January 2015, India's Ministry of Finance updated five detailed pages of 'Guidelines for processing cases of India-specific and regional studies conducted by Multilateral Development Banks': rules about international development

research. Ministries are to be given a chance, in advance, to block research that the government does not want to hear: 'Their comments will include desirability/relevance of the study in Indian context (i.e., whether the study should at all be undertaken).' If there is a 'difference of opinion amongst line Ministries' about whether a proposed study is desirable, the rules specify that a 'final decision would be taken by [a department of the Ministry of Finance] based on the facts and the relevance of the study in the Indian context' – facts that the government is able to apply before the study occurs! If a research plan is approved but government data proves to conflict with independent statistical sources, only the official statistics may be used. In the end, 'final dissemination of the report will be only after approval of Government of India'. International development consents to fit its understanding of the world into a structure that can pass through the many veto points of this approvals process; it is an open empirical question what exactly would happen if it did not.

- Mosse, D., 2005. *Cultivating Development: An Ethnography of Aid Policy and Practice.*
- Mosse, D., 2004. 'Is good policy unimplementable? Reflections on the ethnography of aid policy and practice', *Development and Change*, Vol. 35. No. 4, pp. 639–671.
- Jamieson, D., 2014. *Reason in a Dark Time: Why the Struggle Against Climate Change Failed—and What It Means for Our Future*, Oxford University Press.

An update on survey data for rural open defecation: January 2017: We wrote the first draft of this book in the summer of 2015, and have hoped for the year and a half since that that a high-quality, representative sample survey to track the decline of open defecation over time would emerge, requiring us to substantially revise what we had written. Unfortunately, this has not happened. In this note, we share our suggestions for how to collect high-quality survey data about latrine use, and our reflections on a recent Indian government report on the Swachh Bharat Mission, the Swachh Survekshan Report.

Enough academic and independent surveys of sanitation behaviour among latrine owners in rural India have now been completed that a set of clear lessons has emerged on how to measure open defecation with survey questions. In a working paper titled 'How can a large sample survey monitor open defecation in rural India for the Swachh Bharat Abhiyan?', we analyse data from these independent surveys and make three specific recommendations for how survey questions about open defecation should be asked:

o *balance*: A good survey question explicitly permits both open defecation and latrine use as answers.

o *disaggregation by person*: A good survey question asks each person individually, in the order they are listed on a household roster.

o *specific, recent time frame*: A good survey question refers to a short-term, specific time frame. People may feel more comfortable admitting to open defecation if saying yes for now is not admitting to yes for always.

A question that we recommend, which incorporates balance, disaggregation by person and a specific time frame is: 'Yesterday, did Dean defecate in the open or did Dean use the latrine?' The best approaches to asking this question start with introductory text that makes the respondent feel comfortable and normalizes both answers to the question. One example is: 'I have been to several villages like this one, and I have seen that some people who have latrines use them, and some people who have latrines defecate in the open.' As above, they go on to ask about each person individually: 'What about Dean – yesterday, did Dean defecate in the open or yesterday did Dean use the latrine? And Diane – yesterday, did Diane defecate in the open, or did she use the latrine?'

These well-tested approaches are not the only possibilities, but they are useful for slowing down an interview and creating a shared impression between the surveyor and the respondent that households that own latrines may have some people who use it and others who defecate in the open. In and of themselves, though, they are not sufficient to guarantee an accurate measurement of latrine use; they must be combined with a manageably sized team of motivated surveyors who are held accountable for being correct.

In the second half of 2016, the Ministry of Drinking Water and Sanitation released a Swachh Survekshan Report about rural India. The first part of the report was a presentation of data from the May–June 2015 National Sample Survey Organization (NSSO). These data were conducted in a special rapid survey (that is, they were not collected by being incorporated into the household roster of a survey on consumption or one of the other periodic NSSO surveys). The Report describes the NSSO data as providing information on 'the percentage of people using household/community toilets (of the people having access to toilets)' (p. 4, item 3.1.i). However, this interpretation is not consistent with the NSSO's survey question. The NSSO did not ask a person-level question. In fact, the text provided to surveyors on the NSSO survey form was not phrased as a complete question, so there is not a publicly available, written record of what question surveyors were supposed to say aloud. What is written on the form is instructions to interviewers to record latrine use by demographic groups. To our reading, it is not clear from the NSSO's report whether household members were interviewed at all. It appears likely that latrine use was collected by interviewing a knowledgeable person in the village, at least in some cases. This would have been more convenient for the surveyor, and might have seemed natural to the surveyor because different households did not have their own dedicated survey forms. Instead, all ten households surveyed in each village appear on a single survey form. The survey form is a village-level grid on one page, with household-level rows, and data items as columns.

Several claims in the report support the interpretation that individuals in households were not asked about defecation behaviour, although we emphasize that we cannot be sure from the Report:

o 'Open defecation was measured at the household level through indirect methods' (p. 39).

o 'Information was collected from knowledgeable persons in sample villages on the availability of community toilets for defecation or washing purpose. Further probing was done on the use and cleaning of the community toilets' (p. 41).

o 'While no direct question was asked from the household members whether they went for open defecation, the extent of the same may be measured indirectly as those household members neither using household toilet nor community toilet' (p. 47).

If this is true, the data is likely to contain large non-sampling error, that is, over-reporting of latrine use. The one-page format would make over-reporting convenient for any village-level respondent, who is probably a local official with a perceived incentive to tell government representatives what he believes they want to hear.

Even if an interview were conducted with each household, the data would be unlikely to be reliable: While the survey form does not state the particular questions asked, the numerical blanks correspond to four groups of people ('old', 'adult males', 'adult females' and 'children') rather than to individuals; the description of the item is unbalanced ('number of household members using toilet/community toilet') rather than making a balanced mention of latrine use and open defecation; and the question does not specify any reference period of time (e.g., yesterday, usual, always, ever). Each of these features makes over-reporting latrine use easy for the surveyor and would make claiming to use a latrine appear expected from a respondent.

The second and main part of the Report was a new survey conducted specifically for the Swachh Survekshan Report: 'The survey, carried out by the Quality Council of India and fittingly named as "Swachh Survekshan", was conducted between 20 May 2016 and 21 June 2016, spanning across 75 districts and covering more than 70,000 households.' These districts were chosen purposively to be high-performing districts; they are not representative of India. No villages were surveyed in Uttar Pradesh, Bihar, Andhra or Jharkhand, despite the fact that these states are home to a third of the Indians who defecate in the open.

Rather than measuring open defecation by asking a balanced, disaggregated question about a specific time, the Swachh Survekshan asked an unbalanced question at the household level. It later asked about frequency of open defecation, but only after the answer to the main question had been recorded. Therefore, it would have missed an important number of cases of open defecation among latrine owners.

News reporting on the survey missed these details, sometimes calling the 2016 data on high-performing districts representative of India, sometimes conflating the two surveys (the opening letter from the minister also appears to make this error, in 'Report 2016 of NSSO'), almost never reflecting critically about the survey question in the appendix of the Report. Reports almost always interpreted these numbers as evidence that the Swachh Bharat Mission is succeeding when it actually provides very little evidence either way. For further reading on a latrine use survey:

o Coffey, D. and D. Spears, 2014. 'How can a large sample survey monitor open defecation in rural India for the Swatch Bharat Abhiyan?'

o Ministry of Drinking Water and Sanitation, 2016. 'Swachh Survekshan Gramin 2016'.

o   National Sample Survey Office, 2016. 'Swachhta Status Report', Ministry of Statistics and Programme Implementation.

o   Spears, D. and N. Srivastav, 30 September 2016. 'Churu, the hotspot for Swachh Bharat', *Business Standard*.

Chapter 9

•   Deaton, A., 2013. *The Great Escape: Health, Wealth, and the Origins of Inequality*. Princeton: Princeton University Press.

•   Gordon, R.J., 2012. 'Is US economic growth over? Faltering innovation confronts the six headwinds', Working Paper No. 18315, National Bureau of Economic Research.

•   Crimmins, E.M., 2015. 'Lifespan and healthspan: Past, present, and promise', *The Gerontologist*, Vol. 55, No. 6, pp. 901–911.

•   Gupta, A. and D. Spears. 'Increasing Average Exposure to Open Defecation in India 2001–2011', r.i.c.e. working paper.

•   Das, J. and J. Hammer, 2004. 'Strained mercy: Quality of medical care in Delhi', *Economic & Political Weekly*, pp. 951–961.

•   Currie, J., W. Lin and J. Meng, 2014. 'Addressing antibiotic abuse in China: An experimental audit study', *Journal of Development Economics*, Vol. 110, pp. 39–51.

•   Kapur, A., V. Srinivas and P.R. Choudhury, 2016. 'Swachh Bharat Mission – Gramin', Accountability Initiative Budget Brief 2016-2017, accountabilityindia.in. This budget brief also includes the details that we cite about Accountability Initiative's rural survey, including on awareness of sanitation promoters. 'In the median case' refers to the fact that the survey asked about two possible sanitation promotion jobs and ten districts, for twenty observations.

•   **p. 227: 10,000 times as large.** There are about 250 million households in India. A clustered sample survey of 25,000 households would be more than enough to be constructed to be representative of several large or important states (or parts of states) and of India as a whole; this is approximately the order of magnitude of the rural sample size of the India Human Development Survey, and a useful latrine survey sample would not need to be so large.

- Examples of culture influencing demographic outcomes:
    - Sex preference: Barcellos, S.H., L.S. Carvalho and A. Lleras-Muney, 2014. 'Child Gender and Parental Investments in India: Are Boys and Girls Treated Differently?', *American Economic Journal: Applied Economics*, Vol. 6, No. 1, pp. 157–189.
    - Alcohol-related mortality: Guillot, M., N. Gavrilova and T. Pudrovska, 2011. 'Understanding the "Russian mortality paradox" in Central Asia: Evidence from Kyrgyzstan', *Demography*, Vol. 48, No. 3, pp. 1081–1104.
    - Catholicism and fertility: Westoff, C.F. and E.F. Jones, 1979. 'The end of "Catholic" fertility', *Demography*. Vol. 16, No. 2, pp. 209–17.
    - Religiosity and intended fertility: Hayford, S.R. and S.P. Morgan, 2008. 'Religiosity and fertility in the United States: The role of fertility intentions', *Social Forces*, Vol. 86, No.3, pp. 1163–1188.
- Hathi, P., D. Spears and D. Coffey, 2016. 'Can collective action strategies motivate behaviour change to reduce open defecation in rural India?', *Waterlines*, Vol. 35 No.2, pp. 118–135.
- Glover, J., 2000. *Humanity: A Moral History of the Twentieth Century*, Yale.
- Singer, P., 1981. *The Expanding Circle*, Oxford: Clarendon Press.
- Spears, D., 2015. 'Greene's *Moral Tribes* and Cooperation and Conflict in India', *Economic & Political Weekly*.
- Deshpande, A. and D. Spears, 2016. 'Who Is the Identifiable Victim? Caste and Charitable Giving in Modern India', *Economic Development and Cultural Change*, Vol. 64, No. 2, pp. 299–321.
- **p. 236: teachers, who often come from high-ranking castes.** Teachers have traditionally come from upper castes, and

particularly from Brahmin castes. Some evidence that this may still be the case is that rural households that report knowing a teacher in the IHDS are more than twice as likely to be Brahmin as rural households in which no one knows a teacher. By a wide margin, across India, rural Brahmins are the social group that is most likely to report practising untouchability. Chapters 3 and 4 explained why people who practise untouchability are particularly unlikely to promote affordable latrines.

- Thaler, R.H. and C.R. Sunstein, 2003. 'Libertarian paternalism', *American Economic Review*, Vol. 93, No.2, pp. 175–179.
  Sunstein, C.R. and R.H. Thaler, 2003. 'Libertarian paternalism is not an oxymoron', *University of Chicago Law Review*, pp.1159–1202.

  The systematic catalogue of successful nudges is another form of technocratic tool kit which, just like public health or public economic theory, has an impressive track record of being usefully correct in many situations. It is understandable to read these results and hope that if we could only find the right nudge, we could transform rural sanitation in India too. There is a well-known sanitation example from Thaler and Sunstein's book: One European airport found that much less clean-up of urine was required in men's restrooms when an image of a fly to target was included in the urinals. We imagine that this nudge probably did succeed in its context, but it would not have improved conditions in European restrooms if travellers' widely shared deliberative judgement were that the floor is the only acceptable place to urinate in an airport.

- **p. 236: approaches from marketing or psychology.** This does not mean that there is no room for psychology and behavioural economics to contribute to reducing open defecation. We are certain that there is, although the principles that emerge as successful in rural India may differ from those that work in experiments on North American undergraduates. It is unfortunately true that comparatively little social psychology has studied the dynamics of casteism and ritual purity in rural India, relative to the number of people harmed. The fact that there are so many useful studies of race in the US underscores how much psychologists could help uncover about the dynamics of caste and casteism. Perhaps the importance of open defecation can mark a good occasion for more behavioural economists and social psychologists to begin doing so.

- Aggarwal, A., J. Drèze and A. Gupta, 2015. 'Caste and the Power Elite in Allahabad', *Economic & Political Weekly*, Vol. 50, No. 6, p. 45.
- **p. 238: gradual urbanization.** Munshi, K. and M. Rosenzweig, 2016. 'Networks and misallocation: Insurance, migration, and the rural-urban wage gap', *The American Economic Review*, Vol. 106, No. 1, pp. 46–98.

Acknowledgements

Many people contributed to this book and to the research and thinking behind it. We have much to acknowledge and much gratitude. As always, the ways in which it is lacking are despite our friends' best efforts and are our fault alone. Having your name in these acknowledgements certainly does not imply that you agree with everything we wrote, and that has been useful too because often we have been wrong.

First and most importantly, we thank the thousands of people throughout India who have talked with us and our research team, sometimes for hours, about what open defecation, latrines and life in villages are like for them. This book is our best effort to retell the stories they told us.

We thank Ajitha, our supportive and helpful editor at HarperCollins, who was always enthusiastic about saying yes and making things possible. We also thank Jean Drèze, who gave us early moral support for writing this book, as we sat on the steps of a university in Delhi, even though he knew what writing a book entailed. Alix Zwane, Louis Boorstin, Jan Willem Rosenboom and Radu Ban, in rough chronological order, all thought that the r.i.c.e. team was worth investing in. Anne Case, Angus Deaton, Jeff Hammer and Sara McLanahan taught us more than we can plausibly acknowledge here about how to do this work. The Economics and Planning Unit of the Indian Statistical Institute, Delhi Centre, has been kind enough to host us in India over the past two years as we wrote this book and we are grateful for Chetan Ghate's friendly enthusiasm and support.

Several friends, colleagues and family members have been kind enough to read this and help us improve it: Yamini Aiyar, Radu Ban, Ben Blosch, Louis Boorstin, Mark Budolfson, Robert Chambers, Lynn Coffey, Robert Coffey, Carrie Crompton, April Geruso, Mike Geruso, Jacob Goldin, Aashish Gupta, Payal Hathi, Jan Willem Rosenboom, Sangita Vyas. Your comments and conversation were invaluable. A big thank you to the students of Mark Budolfson's graduate policy seminar at UVM and Prerna Singh's class at Brown who read and commented on a draft. Juan Costain, Josephine Duh, Mike Geruso, Jeff Hammer, Nidhi Khurana, Avinash Kishore, Sneha Lamba, Nicholas Lawson, Nikhil Srivastav and Amit Thorat collaborated with us to learn many of the conclusions we wrote this book to share.

We also owe a deep debt to our friends in Sitapur. Through a small NGO, we were introduced in 2011 to the family who would take us in and help us navigate rural Uttar Pradesh. They were a special couple: Mr Sharma started his career as a pharmaceutical representative, became a journalist and eventually devoted himself to social work. For his efforts towards the public good he was deeply respected by an uncommonly large part of an otherwise bitterly divided society. His wife taught Urdu at a government college at a time when very few women worked outside the home, and is now retired. Over the years, we watched their daughter grow from a giggling student to a lehenga-clad bride with red bangles from wrist to elbow to now a doting mother. We are especially grateful to the Sharmas for introducing us to Baby Parveen Qureshi, our research assistant, whom they have known since she was a girl. Thank you, Baby, for everything you have taught us. Sadly, Mr Sharma died unexpectedly in June 2016. We would have loved to have had the chance to give him a copy of this book.

Our r.i.c.e. colleagues have literally lived this research and this book with us, very often in the same home, which always maintained its character despite the location and amenities changing frequently throughout India. Aashish Gupta, Payal Hathi, Nidhi Khurana, Nikhil Srivastav, Sangita Vyas – it seems silly merely to thank you. Keep doing good things.

If the rest of you will indulge it, we thank one another.

Awarded the

Joseph W. Elder Prize
in the Indian Social Sciences

by the American Institute of Indian Studies and
published with the Institute's generous support.